THE STORY OF
TOOLS
HOW THEY BUILT OUR WORLD
AND SHAPED MAN'S LIFE

JAMES POLING

THE STORY OF

TOOLS

HOW THEY BUILT OUR WORLD

AND SHAPED MAN'S LIFE

GROSSET & DUNLAP
PUBLISHERS · NEW YORK

F

Copyright © 1969 by James Poling
First Edition
Library of Congress Catalog Card No. 69-12623
ISBN: 0-448-26117-0
All Rights Reserved
Published simultaneously in Canada by
George J. McLeod Limited, Toronto
Printed in the United States of America

CONTENTS

LIST OF ILLUSTRATIONS

THE STORY OF

TOOLS

HOW THEY BUILT OUR WORLD
AND SHAPED MAN'S LIFE

PART 1

1

THE ONLY TOOLMAKER

TOOLS are so commonplace we seldom give them a thought. But were it not for tools we would still be primitive cave dwellers. It is only because of man's ability to make tools that we've been able to build the world in which we now live. Thus, the story of tools is not just a history of mechanical developments. To a large extent it is also the story of human progress. Thomas Carlyle wrote, "Man is a tool-using animal. Weak in himself, he has to straddle out his legs lest the very winds supplant him. Nevertheless, man can use tools, can devise tools. With these even the granite mountain melts into dust before him. . . . Without tools man is nothing. With tools he is all."

Right as he was, Carlyle should have made it clearer that man isn't "all" merely because he is a tool user. Man has become what he is because he is the *only* creature who makes tools.

After all, other animals *use* tools too. To name a few, there are termite-eating chimpanzees that use sticks to dig into termite nests to reach their prey. Gorillas sometimes pull branches loaded with fruit within reach with hooked sticks. Hungry sea otters use stones to hammer clams open. Some vultures shatter tough-shelled ostrich eggs with stones. There are finches that use cactus spines to pry insects from their burrows.

Unlike men, though, none of them manufactures the tool it works with, or ever tries to improve it. Nor do other animals ever stock up on their tools, or carry any with them as men do. Instead, they discard them at the end of each job, and then have to hunt around for a new stone or stick when they next need one.

The most important difference, naturally, is that of all the tool-using animals man is the *only* one that also manufactures tools. This is why the story of civilization began when our primitive ancestors fashioned their first crude tools. Then, and only then, did man's way of life begin to differ from the lives of the beasts around him. With tools man civilized himself and found ways to harness the forces of nature and to alter the face of the globe to meet his needs.

If he had to rely on his body alone, prehistoric man would almost surely have gone the way of the dinosaur and other extinct animals. He had no fur pelt to protect him from bitter cold. He wasn't particularly fleet of foot. Because he lacked the protective coloration of, say, the snow leopard, his enemies could easily spot him. He didn't have the elephant's tough hide, nor the body armor of the turtle or armadillo. His eyesight, hearing, and sense of smell weren't especially acute, so he was less able than most creatures to detect the menacing approach of predatory animals. All in all, when he began to roam the earth he was a comparatively weak, puny creature, very intelligent when compared to other animals, but ill-equipped for either escape or self-defense.

Because he used his intellect to decide what was needed for protection and then made the tools to do the job, man survived. Tools became his powerful "third hand"—artificial extensions of his body that immensely increased his strength and capabilities. With them, he learned in time how to push, pull, tear, cut, twist, gouge, and shape any material with which he chose

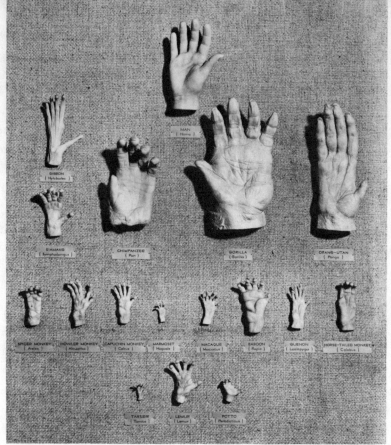

Hands of the primates.

to work, were it wood, stone, or metal. These materials were harder, tougher, stronger, and less subject to fatigue than any animal's flesh, muscle, and bone. Man was able to devise weapons (a specialized form of tool) to defend himself as well as implements for improving his living conditions. Some primitive tools—a stone ax, for instance—served both purposes.

There are three reasons why only man can make tools. First, he stands on two feet instead of four, which is essential to toolmaking because it frees his arms and hands for work. More important, because of his highly developed brain he is the only animal that can think and reason. This enables him, among other things, to analyze mechanical problems and design the tools necessary to solve them. But his mental inventiveness would be of little use to him were it not for a surprising third factor—his thumb!

You've probably never thought about your thumb. Yet, you can press it firmly against any of your fingers. You can even group three fingers in a crescent and press your thumb against all of them. This may seem unimportant to you; but it is one of the most remarkable gifts you possess. You have what is called an "opposable thumb." In the entire animal kingdom you alone have a large, strong thumb that can be placed in firm opposition to your fingers.

By comparison, an ape's thumb, for example, is small, weak, and poorly located in relation to its fingers. Consequently, it is hard for an ape to grasp an object, much harder for it to control one. But with his opposable thumb, a man's hand can easily perform the tasks the brain assigns it. It can become a strong vise, swinging a sledge hammer, or a delicate tweezer, controlling a watchmaker's tiny screwdriver.

Due to his opposable thumb man is said to have the "only toolmaking hands." It is because of the partnership of his unique hands and his unique brain that he survived to build the world we know today.

We think our ancestors first began using their hands to make tools about 2 million years ago. At least, crude tools estimated to be about 1,750,000 years old—far older than any previously uncovered—were recently found in the Olduvai Gorge, a canyon in Tanzania, East Africa. We can't be certain these are man's first tools because we have no guarantee that archaeologists will not find even older ones tomorrow. After all, we are talking about prehistoric times, before man could write. With nothing in writing to tell us about that distant period, we can seldom be sure that our educated guesses about man's beginnings are absolutely accurate.

It isn't until the age of history that we begin to be sure of our facts. This began with the invention of writing, which led to keeping records about the activities and developments of early civilizations. Unfortunately, written accounts that we can decipher go back only about 5,000 years. Yet, the ratio of the time spent on earth by prehistoric man to the time since man began keeping written records is something like the ratio of four hours to one minute. In other words, while we know a great deal about a single minute of man's life span, we know comparatively little about what his forebears did in the long four hours of prehistory.

The little we do know has been pieced together from manmade objects, called artifacts, that archaeologists have found at sites where ancient men lived. What has survived the wear and tear of time is mostly pottery, some weapons, and, above all, an array of tools. The tools give us the best clue to the way the foundations of our modern civilization were laid.

We will never know, of course, what particular inspiration led to making the first tool. Necessity must surely have mothered its invention. Let us suppose, for instance, that 2 million years ago some dawn age men cornered and stoned to death a large deer. With their hands alone it would have been extremely difficult for the hunters to tear the deer into portions they could share.

Suppose, too, that after an unsuccessful attempt to pull a hip joint apart one impatient man picked up a handy stone with a fairly sharp edge and hammered at the joint until its ligaments and tendons parted and it came free in his hand. Then assume that when he tossed the stone aside it struck a rock and had a chip knocked off it, which made its edge even sharper. This might have given birth to the idea that a crude knife could be made by hammering chips off one stone with a harder stone until the first stone had a thin, sharp edge.

Whether or not this was how toolmaking was born, we do know that man's first stone tools were made in just this fashion, by hammering one stone with another. After this crude beginning, what followed was inevitable, man being what he is. We all have a natural desire to do as little physical work as necessary, and primitive man was no exception. Though his brain was not yet fully developed, he, too, wanted to do his work as easily and painlessly as he could. This universal desire kept him thinking about the only things that could help him make life less laborious—more and better tools.

As one archaeologist says, "Nobody knows for how many hundreds of thousands of years dawn man banged his hands around with stone axes that had to be held between the thumb and the fingers. But the pain and discomfort of the hand ax kept nagging at his slowly-developing brain until he got an idea. He put handles on his axes. Since then, as man's thinking has improved his tools have gotten continually better. This endless cycle is still the secret of our material progress."

Definitions of tools vary. Most experts consider any device that does man's *work* for him a tool, and they make no distinction between hand tools and machinery. They believe a machine is simply a tool with moving parts.

The definition is logical and broad enough to cover all varities of tools, which now number no one knows how many millions. To give you some idea of how productive man's inventive genius has been, the head of the U.S. Patent Office resigned in 1833, because he thought the 30,000 patents his office had issued had "virtually exhausted" the possibilities of invention! Yet, by 1900, more than 600,000 additional patents had been granted. The rate has increased so sharply that new patents now average 85,000 a year in this country alone.

Obviously, in a book of this or any length it is impossible to describe even a small fraction of the tools man has produced in a span of almost 2 million years. It is possible, though, to cover the key discoveries and inventions that led to the others. This is all that is necessary to show how man built his present-day material world, with its incredible physical abundance. It is also all that is needed to show how, with the aid of tools, man progressed from an apelike creature to a civilized human being.

2

FROM FIST AX TO PLOW

OUR earliest ancestors almost certainly used tools before they made them. They probably picked up whatever was handy—a sharp stone for a cleaver, a thigh bone for a hammer—then cast it aside. Their inventive genius took root and human progress began only when they got the idea, no one knows how, that it would be to their advantage to keep tools permanently at their sides.

The 1,750,000-year-old Olduvai Gorge tools may be the first ever made. Certainly, it's hard to imagine that any cruder tools could have existed. However, there is a debate about the Olduvai toolmakers' position on man's family tree. Some scholars consider them to be among man's early ancestors. Others think they were similar to man but not true *Hominoids*. (To scientists we are known as *Homo sapiens,* and our ancestors are called *Hominoids.*) For practical purposes, though, the implements found in the Gorge are now believed to mark the beginning of toolmaking and the start of the Stone Age.

The Stone Age is the first of three early stages in man's development. Running from roughly 6,000 to 2 million years ago, the age is so named because most of its tools were made of stone. For the same reason the second stage, from about 2,600 to 6,000 years ago, is known as the Bronze Age. Then follows the Iron Age, the bridge to modern times.

The reason for naming the three ages after their principal toolmaking materials is simple. Their tools, being durable, have survived in better condition than most other things manufactured in those remote days. Since tools tell us a great deal about the skill and knowledge of their makers, most of what we know about man's beginnings has been learned from the tools he produced.

Although the Olduvai implements are called "pebble tools," most of them are somewhat larger than your fist. They are clumsy to hold, and they have only one rough, cutting edge. As all-purpose tools, they were used for such jobs as slicing through tough animal hides, cutting meat into chunks small enough to carry, scraping flesh from skins to be cured, and sharpening the digging sticks with which edible roots and bulbs were unearthed.

To our eyes, pebble tools may look too crude to deserve the name "tool." Yet, they are truly awesome objects when you remember that they were made by the world's first *thinkers,* the first creatures who ever thought of the morrow instead of living just for the moment. Pebble tools also show us how limited man's thinking was in the beginning. It was more than a million years before he could think of a better tool.

During those eons, his mind developed more slowly than a glacier moves. Eventually the stones on his rock anvils began to be hammered into shape with greater skill. They fitted his hand more snugly, grew increasingly efficient, and some of them were designed for specific jobs. Through trial and error and with experience, dawn man was gradually learning, slowly expanding his thinking capacity.

As might be expected, his first new tool was simply an improved pebble tool. Called a fist ax, it too, served him for thousands of centuries as an all-purpose tool. First manufactured

Early men used stone tools like these for chopping and cutting. The smooth ax in the lower left corner comes from the latter part of the Stone Age, while the other examples are older and less finely worked.

some 450,000 years ago, the fist ax was soon common from South Africa to England, Greece, and India. It was usually about 12 inches long, easy to grip, and shaped like your two hands placed palm to palm. With two straight, sharp edges that tapered to a point, it was useful for chopping, cutting, and scraping. The point could also be used as a chisel, to drill holes, and to do such jobs as splitting a small bone and hollowing it out to make a rough spoon.

The appearance of the fist ax in widely separated areas at roughly the same time is typical of many early tools, and is seen as proof that none of them was invented by a single individual. Stone Age men were too few and too thinly spread across the globe to be able to pass word of a new invention from tribe to tribe. It is believed that toolmaking developed along the same lines in many different regions because of a general rise in Stone Age man's mental level, wherever he lived.

Early men made simple tools of ivory, bone, wood, and even antlers, as well as a variety of stones. They soon found that flint—a brittle stone that chips easily, leaving a knifelike edge, and which can be hammered into almost any shape—was the material best suited to their needs. This led to the use of so much flint that late in the Stone Age surface supplies of it ran short. Then, the only way to meet the demand for the stone was to mine it.

This was probably the most difficult technical challenge man had yet faced. But he had, by then, acquired the skill to meet it, as the remains of numerous old flint mines prove. There is one in England, for example, with a 40-foot-deep main shaft from which tunnels run out to seams of flint, like spokes from a wheel. It was dug with deer-antler picks and shovels carved from the shoulder blades of oxen, by miners who lighted their way with cup-shaped stone lamps containing wicks that were fed by tallow. All things considered, the mine is a remarkable engineering feat.

Flint mining was perfected between 15,000 and 10,000 B.C., the years in which man made the transition from the Old to the New Stone Age. In this era—from 10,000 to 4000 B.C.—our primitive forefathers devised new technologies and new ways of living, even though they remained dependent on stone tools.

The New Stone Age produced only one major toolmaking advance. It was the use of abrasives—sand, pumice, and coarse-grained rocks—to grind and polish flint tools into much more useful shapes, with far sharper edges. This may not sound impressive. It has been estimated that the cutting edge made with the use of abrasives was one hundred times sharper than the cutting edge obtained by the chipping process. Moreover, abrasives made it easier to make tools for particular jobs. As a result, drills, chisels, hatchets, hammers, and saws with stone teeth set in wooden frames were added to man's tool kit.

A variety of razor-sharp flint knives were also added. Some were for carving large objects, others for whittling small needles, pins, and fishhooks from ivory and bone, still others for shaping spear and harpoon heads. Amazingly, there was even a finely honed surgical knife. It was used to remove slivers of bone from a fractured skull in an operation called trepanning, which is still performed.

Still another knife was made to slice leather into thin thongs to be used to sew cured hides into garments or to tie objects together. Some authorities think the thongs may have given men the idea of lashing a stone cutting edge to a wooden handle to make a true ax.

However the idea was born, users of the ax must have been startled to discover that it accomplished far more than they had intended. While the handle made chopping easier on their hands, as they had hoped, for some mysterious reason it also multiplied the strength of their arms. With a long-handled ax, men found they could chop trees down and split and shape logs with an ease which they had never dreamed was possible—and which unquestionably played a major role in founding the craft of carpentry.

What had happened was that the axmakers, without knowing it, had stumbled on a basic law of mechanics. It was the law of the lever, which holds that a little effort over a long distance does just as much work as a great effort over a short distance. The ax handle was a lever that greatly lengthened the axman's reach. This lengthened the distance the axhead traveled, allowing it to gain a momentum and striking force that were impossible to attain with a hand-held fist ax. Thus the chips flew twice as fast as they did when a fist ax was swung through a short, arm-length arc. More will be said about the law of the lever later, when the basic laws of mechanics are discussed.

As a toolmaker, primitive man was progressing faster than he knew. Without realizing it he had discovered the lever, which, even now, is one of the most important mechanical devices employed. His workshop contained most of the basic hand tools we still use.

Even so, it is not for its improved tools that the New Stone Age is most famous. Its greatest achievement was the development of agriculture and the domestication of sheep, cattle, dogs, and goats. Most scholars believe that without these fundamental technological advances in human history, we could never have reached our present civilized state.

To understand why, you must realize that before the introduction of farming, no man was ever sure of where he would get his next meal. To survive, he had to devote most of his waking hours to hunting, fishing, and gathering wild fruits, nuts, and cereal grains. When game was scarce and plant foods out of season, he had to spend long, desperate hours grubbing for edible roots and bulbs, using a crude digging stick to break up the hard earth. Every single day, almost his entire time and energy was spent meeting his stomach's demands.

Agriculture transformed man from a food hunter to a food producer. Since a farmer could produce more food than his own family needed, his surplus food could be used to feed other people. This relieved them of the need to hunt for food and left them free to do other things. They had free time to devote to the invention of new mechanical devices and technical processes, and to the new jobs these advances created. This freedom—possible only when there is a surplus of food—is the keystone of civilization.

This is as true today as it was in the remote past. If our farmers didn't produce surplus foods no one would be free to work in a factory, teach, peer through a microscope, make and enforce laws, practice medicine, become a comedian, write a book, or do any other type of work. He'd be too busy hunting food for his family.

Now you know why the New Stone Age has been called the "greatest of all chapters in human history." It was the age in which man's mind began to soar because it was no longer his stomach's slave, the period that saw man emerge from savagery. As we will see, it was all made possible by a tool whose revolutionary importance is now seldom appreciated: the plow.

It's uncertain whether the domestication of animals preceded farming or the two went hand-in-hand. Whichever the case, it's easy to imagine how what we call animal husbandry began. Wild dogs would soon become attached to men who tossed them bones. Baby wild sheep, goats, and cattle could easily be caught for pets. When they matured they would breed. In short order they would produce flocks and herds that would provide constant supplies of meat, milk, cheese, fur, and wool.

We know that farming was in existence in some parts of the world around 7000 B.C., but not what inspired it. A common guess is that leftover seeds were thrown on garbage heaps that served as fertilizers. The luxuriant growths that followed were noticed with wonder by intelligent, observant eyes, and curiosity led to experiments in planting seeds. It could have been that simple.

We learned that farming sprang up on opposite sides of the globe at the same time only a couple of years ago, when it was discovered that in the heart of Mexico there had been farming in 7000 B.C., too. At the moment, all we know about prehistoric Mexican farming is that the main crops were pumpkins, peppers, avocados, and squash.

Before this discovery it was thought that the "Fertile Crescent" was the sole cradle of agriculture. The Crescent is the region curving like a huge quarter moon around the eastern end of the Mediterranean Sea, and it includes the Nile River delta and the valleys of the Tigris and Euphrates Rivers. Now largely desert, it was excellent farming country in earlier times. Heavy rainfalls brought annual floods in the river valleys. The barley, wheat, peas, and lentils native to the region flourished in the fresh layers of rich soil, or silt, the floods deposited each year.

The first farmers in the Crescent are thought to have simply scattered grain on the silt after the flood waters receded. The birds that gobbled up their seeds taught them to drive cattle back and forth across their fields to trample the seeds into the

ground. This, however, was a hit-and-miss method that didn't
work well, so they tried tilling the soil with their digging sticks.

When this, too, proved unsatisfactory, necessity mothered
the invention of the first plow. It was a Y-shaped forked stick
with a stone plowshare lashed to the base of the Y. By pushing
it, a man could gouge a crude furrow. It was such hard work
that it exhausted a man to plow the land needed to feed his
own family. Then the harness plow was devised. It was pulled
by two men while a third controlled it with the help of handles
arching up from a curved plowshare of improved design. The
next step, obviously, was to harness oxen to the plow, using a
yoke not unlike the ox-yoke in use today.

Then the civilizing process began in earnest. Oxen made it
possible to cultivate large tracts of lands and to grow generous
surpluses of food. To till fields and tend flocks and herds, men
had to stop roving and settle down. This led to the first villages.
They began as small clusters of houses within walking distance
of their owners' fields and pastures. Yet, several of them later
grew into the world's first great cities.

While some of the villages in the Fertile Crescent were
merely groups of huts made of woven branches plastered with
clay, others had more substantial houses built of wood or sun-
dried bricks or a combination of both. Here was proof that
surplus food was freeing man to develop new skills and crafts
—in this instance, carpentry and masonry.

Men freed by farming began putting their minds to work in a
variety of ways. Some devised scythes and sickles for harvesting grain. Others invented millstones for grinding grain into
flour. Still others designed ovens for baking the flour. Some
men also learned how to weave baskets in which to carry and
store the grain.

One form of weaving may have led to another, for primitive

Domesticated animals were used to pull wooden plows about 8,000 years ago.

looms and spindles appeared at this time too. The weaving of cloth quickly progressed, enabling men to spin coarse threads of dog hairs as well as wool, then make blankets which they colored with berry juices and other natural dyes. Rope was woven too. Then an unsung genius, possibly a farmer plagued by straying cattle, invented the lasso and put it to use thousands of years before it became the symbol of the cowboy on the Western Plains.

The plow that made these technical advances possible was a civilizing influence in other ways too. For people to live together in an orderly manner in the villages, they had to develop the foundation stones of government, a simple code of laws. Villagers also had to learn how to live and play together as neighbors. This led to the growth of some of the patterns of social living we still follow, including, some think, dancing, games and sports, feasting, gift-giving, even beer drinking.

Finally, since village life was safer and much more secure than the food hunter's existence, people lived longer. This launched a population explosion that has not yet ended. Indeed, when farming began in 7000 B.C. the estimated population of the entire world was approximately 7 million, less than that of New York City today.

When man entered the New Stone Age 12,000 years ago he was a savage fighting for survival. Emerging from it 6,000 years later, he was no longer a savage, and his survival was assured. In fact, outside of the more advanced industrial countries, most villagers today are still working at the jobs he invented, still living in much the same way—and still using much the same sort of plow!

PUTTING FIRE TO WORK

FIVE stone-and-clay hearths were found in 1960 in a cave dwelling in the south of France. The cave was also littered with the bones of primitive wolves and saber-toothed cats. According to archaeologists, they were the bones of animals roasted by cave men some 750,000 years ago over fires the cave men themselves ignited. This means the ashes found on the hearths were the remains of the oldest known man-made fires.

Surprisingly, there is reason to believe that the cave's inhabitants were descended from toolmakers who once lived in the Olduvai Gorge. Why the cave men's ancestors walked from East Africa to France is anyone's guess. Whether they carried the secret of fire-making with them or learned it along the way is also unknown, as is almost everything else about man's first use of fire.

We know only that dawn man was born into a world of flame and brimstone, when active volcanoes were fairly common. The Great African Rift Valley, a 4,000-mile-long gash in the earth's crust with the Olduvai Gorge near its southern tip, was created by volcanic eruptions. It was a time, too, when lightning-ignited brush and forest fires were almost certainly much more numerous than they now are. We can be sure that dawn man knew fire and sometimes had to flee from it.

No one knows, though, when he first learned to use embers from nature's frightening fires to light campfires to keep himself warm, cook his meat, and scare off night-prowling animals. Once he'd learned the trick, we assume that thereafter each tribe had a "fire-bearer"—a man responsible for keeping the tribe's "match-box" of glowing coals alive. When the tribe was on the move, he probably carried the coals in a clay container, smoldering under a blanket of green leaves.

How men learned to start fires on their own is another mystery. Perhaps they first learned by rubbing two dry sticks together. But it seems more likely that the original discovery was an accidental by-product of toolmaking. Hammering flint was bound to produce showers of sparks. The sparks needed only to fly into dry moss or parched grass for a primitive toolmaker to discover one way of starting fires. Because flint sparks so readily it remained in use through the era of the flintlock rifle and is still used in cigarette lighters. The common match is only about 140 years old.

When he learned to make and control fire, man obtained one of his most priceless tools. Fire gave him the key to the conquest of nature because it produces chemical changes in natural raw materials. Without it, for instance, we couldn't separate, or smelt, pure metals from their ores; and without metal the world as we know it would not exist. Thus, it was fire that introduced the Bronze Age, because fire created the science of metallurgy: the art of reducing ores to metal, of making alloys, and of working metal into usable objects.

The Bronze Age opened in the Near East around 4000 B.C., then spread through the rest of the inhabited world. Yet copper, not bronze, was the first metal to be put to use. This was because malachite—a copper ore so rich it sometimes yields 50 percent pure metal—was abundant in the Near East. Furthermore, it was easily obtained. Malachite, usually found on or near the surface of the ground, is easy to spot because the ore is bright green. It is so colorful, in fact, that women used a malachite paste as a cosmetic for painting their eyelids long before men began smelting it.

It is easy to imagine how men learned that intense heat would cause metal to flow from certain rocks. You can picture them seated around roaring fires banked with malachite boulders, watching with amazement as globules of copper dripped from the rocks into the flames. Raking the fires' dead ashes later, they would be equally surprised to find that the liquid from the rocks had not gone up in smoke but had hardened into gleaming metallic beads. Even in recent years prospectors in the copper-rich Congo made it a practice to search the ashes of native campfires for telltale beads of metal.

A copper tool had only one advantage over a stone tool. If a stone axhead broke, it was useless, whereas a copper one could be remelted and recast. Soon after copper-smelting began, it became obvious that the metal was too soft to make good tools. Then it was found that a mixture, or alloy, of copper and tin produced a much harder metal: bronze. No one knows how it happened. It is reasonable to suppose, however, that the alloy was discovered through the accidental smelting of ores that contained a mixture of copper and tin, which aren't uncommon. In any event, bronze quickly replaced copper for tool-making.

For a time above ground outcroppings of ore, which were easy to work, supplied all the metal that was needed. Exposed rocks were split by kindling fires against them, then dousing their heated surfaces with cold water. Later, surface supplies of ore ran out, just as flint had disappeared years before. Once again, man had to resort to mining.

The oldest ore mine we know of, on the Sinai Peninsula, was mined in 2600 B.C. More impressive, though, is a somewhat later one in Austria. It shows the great progress made in mining since its Stone Age beginnings. The mine's 300-foot-long galleries are almost modern in their engineering. Not only are they securely shored up with massive timbers, they also have ventilation shafts!

Although bronze was in fairly general use by 2000 B.C., its production was handicapped by the fact that ore could be smelted only in highly inefficient open-hearth fires. Hearths were usually built on windy hillsides in the often-vain hope that updrafts would fan their flames and produce the heat needed to melt metal. It wasn't until about 400 years later that the bellows, or "blow-bag," was invented. With it, smelting furnaces could be built, which put the manufacture of bronze on a more practical footing.

A bellows feeds a strong current of air into a furnace and fans the coals on which the ore rests to a white-hot temperature. In its simplest form, a bellows consists of two boards joined with flexible leather sides to form a bag that serves as an air chamber. When the boards are pulled apart, air is sucked into the chamber through an inward-opening valve. When a bellows operator squeezes the boards together, he forces air into a furnace through a nozzle.

With the smelting furnace more copper and tin could be produced and, naturally, more bronze tools could be made. Some were hammered out on anvils by blacksmiths working with another new invention: tongs for handling red-hot metal. Some were made by pouring, or casting, molten metal in open clay or stone molds. The finest tools were made by the *cire perdue* process.

In this process a model of a tool was carefully carved in wax, then coated with clay. When the clay was baked it hardened into pottery, but the wax melted and ran out of the mold. Molten bronze was then poured into the cavity. When the metal hardened the mold was broken, revealing a tool having the exact shape as the wax model.

Using the *cire perdue* process, Bronze Age metalworkers were able to cast most of the then-known tools and many new ones as well, including carpenters' rasps, cold chisels that cut both stone and metal, and even safety pins and razors. They also used the process to manufacture swords, daggers, battle-axes, helmets, shields, and breastplates.

Typical instruments of the Bronze Age were the ax, an awl with a haft of antler, the needle, the fibula, or simple form of safety pin, and the sickle blade.

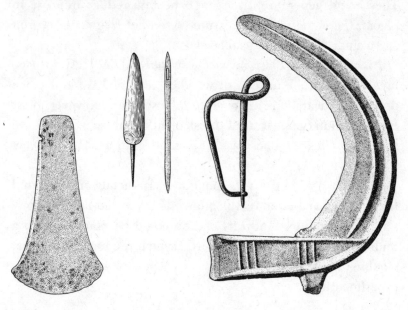

But bronze was expensive to produce—as it still is—and only the rich could afford it. The poor had to struggle with stone, bone, and wooden tools. For the poor to benefit and for metallurgy to make a major advance, it would be necessary to use a much cheaper, much more abundant metal: iron.

Men had known that iron was buried in the earth since 2800 B.C. They even knew that it fell from the sky in the form of meteorites; in some sections of the Near East it was called "the heaven-sent metal." (In modern times, a meteor that fell in Greenland provided an Eskimo village with iron for more than a century!)

However, knowing about iron was one thing, making use of it another. Iron ore wasn't affected by open-hearth fires, so experiments in smelting it had to await the invention of the bellows. The first experiments, made around 1400 B.C., were discouraging because smelting furnaces couldn't melt iron. They could generate only enough heat to reduce iron ore to bloom, the name given a mixture of red-hot fragments of iron and a cinderlike material called slag.

To melt iron a blast furnace was needed. A blast furnace uses coke for fuel, instead of wood or coal, and is fed a fierce draft of preheated air to generate intense heat. However, blast furnaces didn't appear until the sixteenth century A.D., and the first truly effective one wasn't invented until a comparatively few years ago, in 1735.

Through trial and error, though, early metalworkers found that if they hammered the bloom while it was red-hot the stony slag would shatter, and bits of iron could be pounded into a usable lump. But it was a soft iron which produced tools that wouldn't hold a cutting edge. Bronze Age man had to continue experimenting.

A foot-operated bellows pumped air into the early furnaces to intensify heat and smelt iron ore in 1400 B.C.

It took him centuries, but he finally learned that if he repeatedly reheated and rehammered a lump of iron, it changed into low-grade steel. This was because with each reheating the lump received an additional coat of carbon from the coal in the furnace, and steel is a mixture of carbon and iron. Metalworkers then found that plunging hot steel into cold water, a process called quenching, made the metal even harder. They also learned that tempering—allowing hot steel to cool very slowly—had a different effect. It made the metal tougher and less brittle.

Metallurgy reached this stage around 600 B.C. Although iron tools had been in use for some time, this is when the Iron Age truly began. From 600 B.C. on, iron tools that were both harder and tougher than bronze were in general use by rich and poor. They were all forged tools, hammered out of red-hot iron by blacksmiths, then ground and filed into their finished form. Not until the invention of the blast furnace could tools be made of cast iron poured into molds.

Blacksmiths of the Iron Age soon acquired remarkable skill in forging new tools as well as improving old ones. They constructed dies for making files with which to finish off the rough products of their anvils. They invented wire-drawing dies and pulled red-hot metal into wire through holes bored into the dies with iron drill bits, which were also their handiwork. They designed special anvils for making nails.

For cutting iron, they invented hacksaws with metal frames that had sharp gem stones set into them for teeth. Industrial diamonds are still used for tough cutting jobs today. Saws with similar teeth were made for cutting rocks into building blocks in quarries. Blacksmiths also designed some tools that have never been bettered. For example, the shoe repairman's knife and today's bricklayer's trowel are practically duplicates of those then used.

In weaponry, too, smiths were both skilled and clever. They forged tempered iron swords that wouldn't shatter when a powerful blow was struck, as bronze swords often did. They made throwing spears with iron heads and wooden shafts that were cleverly held together by wooden pins that broke on impact, destroying the weapons so that they would be of no use to the enemy.

The most complex science yet mastered by early man, metallurgy quickly gave rise to a new group of specialists. Making tools was full-time work requiring the services of skilled miners, foundry workers, and blacksmiths. All of them, obvi-

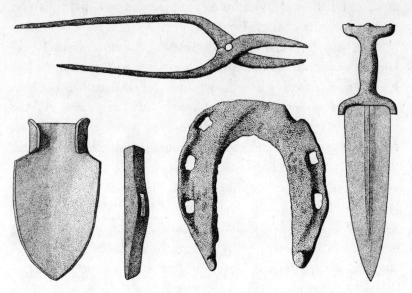

Iron Age implements included this hammer, tongs, plowshare, horseshoe, and dagger.

ously, had to be relieved of the job of growing food. The development of metallurgy was further proof of society's dependence on the farmer.

Metallurgy had its civilizing side effects. Not all villages were located near ore fields, but all of their inhabitants wanted metal tools. This gave villagers a reason to work hard to produce surplus cloth, pottery, grain, furs, ivory, or any other marketable commodity they could exchange for tools. Put another way, metallurgy stimulated the growth of trade and increased production of goods.

It is believed that at the beginning of the Iron Age some blacksmiths took to the road and made tools to order from bars of metal borne by oxen. Apparently, many peddlers also traveled about, trading in tools. Otherwise it would be difficult to account for the exact picture of a Grecian dagger that is carved on a rock in Stonehenge, England.

It is easy to imagine the excitement a visitor from far-off Greece would create in an English village in those days, with his tales of a world the villagers never had dreamed of. It is also easy to overlook the significance of such visits. As the traveling blacksmiths and peddlers went about their business, crossing boundaries and meeting strange people with different ways and customs, they were both teachers and pupils. They taught the strangers they met something about their own culture and technical skills, and returned home with news of the way things were being done in other lands. Without being aware of it, they were really serving humanity in two ways—they were distributing knowledge as well as metal tools.

If the invention of the plow marked the beginning of an organized society, in terms of the village, putting fire to work to produce metal was man's next significant step forward. With metallurgy, the rise of civilization and spread of knowledge and culture began. We all owe a much greater debt to those soot-smudged early Iron Age metalworkers than most of us realize. As a famous archaeologist, Sir Flinders Petrie, said, "while thousands of writers have described the sculptures of ancient Greece, not one has praised the cold chisels that made them possible."

HARNESSING ENERGY

As HUNTERS, primitive men were aware of the tremendous strength of large animals. They felt the howling force of the wind when storms raged. They must have seen large trees swept downstream by swift-flowing rivers. Yet, for more than a million and a half years they did not realize that these powerful forces in nature could be tamed and put to work. Instead, in struggling to survive they used nothing but their own comparatively feeble muscles.

In a few instances, it's true, they found ways to add to their strength and capabilities. The ax handle was one way. Using stout poles as crowbars was another. With the poles they would pry up the edge of an object too heavy to lift, like a rock, shove logs under it, then roll it wherever they wished.

Later, they built sledges for moving heavy loads—an idea born, perhaps, of the practice of dragging slaughtered animals over the ground in their skins. The first sledges were roughly shaped tree trunks. Then ski-like runners were added so the sledges could be pulled over grass, bare earth, and snow, with less friction. There is a Stone Age rock carving in Norway showing a man on a pair of skis surprisingly like those in use now. But we don't know which came first, sledge runners or skis.

A bent bough that snapped back and hit a man in the face

when it was released may have inspired another Stone Age
invention for multiplying human strength, the bow and arrow.
Invented in North Africa about 30,000 years ago, the taut,
springlike bow speedily shot an arrow to its mark with greater
force and much farther than a man could throw his hunting
spear.

The bow also started man on his career as a mechanic able to
build a machine with moving parts. It led directly to the bow
drill, which had moving parts, too. Before its invention, in the
New Stone Age, holes were drilled by twisting the point of a
fist ax or by rolling a stick fitted with a stone point between the
palms of the hands. By looping a bow string around such a
stick and sawing the bow back and forth, New Stone Age man
could drill holes faster and with less effort.

In most instances, though, men struggled through the Stone
Ages solely under their own power, straining their endurance
to the limit. Not until the Bronze and Iron Ages was man's
muscle power gradually replaced, first by the greater strength
of beasts of burden, later by the tireless energies of wind and
water.

We know the wild ass, or donkey, was tamed and put to
work around 3500 B.C. But it's possible that dogs, reindeers,
and camels were used centuries earlier. The ox became man's
helper sometime before 2000 B.C., the horse a couple of centuries later. All were used as pack animals and to draw sledges.
Except for the dogs, the animals were also ridden and used to
raise ore from mines. Contrary to what you would expect, the
horse and donkey were never used for plowing if oxen were
available.

The trouble lay in the only harness then known, a yoke held
in place with a strap passing under the neck. The harness
didn't bother the short-necked ox. Because horses and donkeys

have long necks, the harness strap cut into their windpipes. As a result, they had to hold their heads unnaturally erect to avoid choking, and they could pull with only a fraction of their full strength under the best of circumstances. Hitched to a plow, they were even less efficient.

Twenty-three centuries later the problem was still so far from solution that in the Roman postal service, for example, the legal limit for a two-horse load was 1100 pounds, perhaps one-quarter of the weight a single horse can now pull. The horse collar and the horseshoe finally made it possible to use the strength of the horse in a variety of ways. They were invented only 700 years ago—a good 3,000 years after the animal was tamed.

Nevertheless, Bronze Age men managed to get a fair amount of work out of the horse and donkey. By a happy coincidence, these animals were domesticated at roughly the same time that the wheel and axle appeared, the mechanism that set us on the road to the automobile. But first, of course, there were the cart, the wagon, and the chariot. Even with faulty harnesses, donkeys and horses could pull loads in wheeled vehicles that would have choked them had they tried to draw them on sledges. The wheel made the horse and donkey truly useful beasts of burden to early man. In fact, the wheel was the greatest achievement of ancient carpentry, for we probably owe more to it than to any other mechanical device.

The earliest wheels—some of which had leather tires!—were made of either solid wood or three planks carved to form circles and clamped together with wooden struts. Both forms date back to around 3500 B.C. Both support the belief that the idea of making wheels grew out of the practice of moving heavy objects on log rollers. Wheels with spokes, lighter and easier to pull, weren't designed until 1500 B.C.

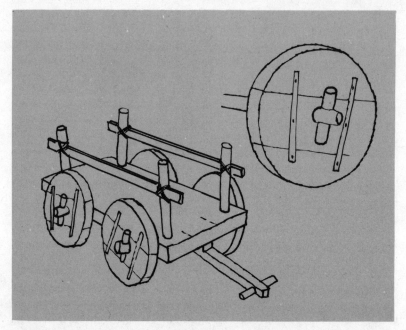

Wheels were used as early as 3500 B.C. in Mesopotamia.

The place of origin of the wheel is uncertain. Like so many basic inventions, it was probably conceived in the Fertile Crescent. China can apparently take credit for the invention of one of the oldest known vehicles, the wheelbarrow, which the Chinese often equipped with a sail. (The two-wheeled cart that is considered symbolic of China, the rickshaw, was actually invented by an American missionary!)

The geographical origin of the wheel is unimportant. What is important is that the wheel wrought more changes in man's world than any other one invention. To understand what wheels mean to us, try to imagine what it would be like if every wheel now turning suddenly refused to budge. All of the machinery in the world would grind to a halt. Everything that's moving would stop. Your life would come to a standstill, too.

You couldn't go anyplace. You couldn't fill your time watching TV because its cameras wouldn't turn. You wouldn't even be able to tell the time because all clocks would stop. Still, you wouldn't have to mow the grass, but that would hardly make up for all you would lose.

Mankind began to feel the tremendous impact of the wheel from the moment it appeared. Horse-drawn vehicles revolutionized the transporation of goods and people, sped up communications, and led to the growth of road networks. The wheel-and-axle principle was also immediately adapted for use in fields having nothing to do with transportation. Immensely useful weight-lifting tools, like the pulley, the windlass, and the capstan, were all invented before the end of the Bronze Age. So too was the hand-cranked grindstone for sharpening tools, which was still being used on American farms in the 1920's.

More important was the potter's wheel, a device so practical that it is still used by craftsmen throughout the world. It was a horizontal circular slab of wood set on a perpendicular axle so that it would spin as freely as the lazy susans on our dinner tables. Under the pressure of a potter's hand, a lump of soft clay centered on the spinning wheel could be shaped into a pot in minutes. Previously, the job had taken hours, for pots were originally built up in layers, out of thin circles of clay. Thus, the potter's wheel initiated the first mechanized industry, because it was the first machine to manufacture a product in quantity for barter or exchange.

Of equal importance was the irrigation wheel. As mankind grew increasingly dependent on the growth of surplus crops, irrigation became more vital. Yet, before the advent of the wheel, farmers had to hand-feed water to irrigation ditches with the help of a *shaduf*. This was a wooden pole with a

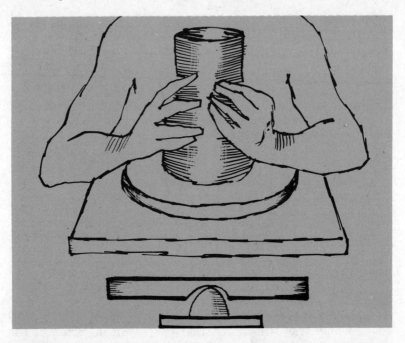

Another early use of the wheel was to make pottery.

bucket on one end and a counterweight on the other. The pole was balanced in a U-shaped groove on an upright post. When the bucket was dipped into a well or a river, the counterweight made it easier for a farmer to lift the filled bucket and empty it into a field.

Then about 250 B.C. a famous Greek inventor and mathematician, Archimedes, invented a new water-raising device. Today Archimedes is best remembered for his dramatic description of the power of the lever, "Give me but a place to stand and a lever, and I can move the world." He was never boastful about his own water-raising device, perhaps because he himself failed to appreciate its importance. Yet, it was an invention almost on a par with the lever and one that was to have an immeasurable impact on all future technology.

The device was a round wooden pole wrapped spirally with

strips of wood that were set on edge, like the threads of a
screw, then tightly encased in boards. Placed in a stream at an
angle and spun by foot, it forced water to climb its spiral
"staircase" and gush out into an irrigation ditch. Though it was
useful to farmers, its vast importance lay in its design. To the
best of our knowledge, Archimedes was the first to employ the
principle of the screw. Every form of screw we now use—a
corkscrew, a meat grinder, or the screw-form blades of a ship's
propeller—derives from his invention.

However, a water wheel invented some 200 years later,
which is still widely used in underdeveloped countries, proved
to be even more efficient than Archimedes' water screw. A

*A camel turns this water wheel in India, used to raise water from
a well and irrigate a farm.*

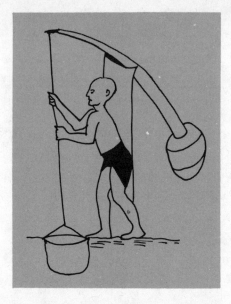

The shaduf *is a device used to help men raise water from the Nile River into the fields above the river level. This ancient Egyptian tool is still used.*

large wheel fitted with buckets was set on a river bank so that it was partially submerged. When it was turned, either by man- or ox-power, its buckets scooped up water and emptied it into an irrigation canal. In itself, this was a simple implement, but it was the first step towards one of man's greatest triumphs.

The next step was the *noria,* another product of the Fertile Crescent. It was a water wheel equipped with paddles as well as buckets. With its paddles, the *noria* would turn without help from man or ox. The flowing current of a river did all the work. It alone was enough to make the wheel revolve endlessly and spill an endless amount of water into an irrigation ditch. With the *noria,* man had at last harnessed and put to work one of nature's greatest forces: water power.

The invention was a great event in engineering history on several counts. While the *noria* was at first an irrigation wheel, within a few centuries mechanics had so altered it that the water power it generated could be used for any number of purposes. They removed its buckets, retained and improved its paddle blades, and put it to work as an out-and-out water wheel. In this role it was soon supplying power to flour mills, drop-forges, saw mills and a variety of small factories.

In fact, in terms of economy, cleanliness, and efficiency, the water wheel is even today considered the best of all methods of power production. This is why thousands of water-powered installations are still in use all over the globe. It is why countless water wheels—in the form of turbines driven by cascades, like Niagara Falls, or water accumulated by huge dams—are even now turning in hydroelectric plants. Indeed, turbines descended from the ancient *noria* produce most of the electricity that makes our world hum.

Bronze Age man must be credited with harnessing still another form of energy. No one knows when the first boat was launched. It was probably no more than a hollowed-out log. We do know that square-rigged sailboats were skimming the Nile no later than 1800 B.C. In the next 1,500 years, as men's mastery of the erratic winds increased, they learned enough seamanship to voyage regularly across the eastern Mediterranean and occasionally to venture as far as the Arabian Sea. It was only a beginning towards putting the wind to work, since centuries would pass before men thought of harnessing the

Archimedes is credited with the invention of this water-raising screw. When the screw was turned, water would climb the screw from a river or well and irrigate a field or a higher level. The screw was a spiral of wood wrapped around a beam and encased in boards.

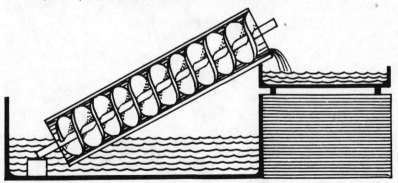

wind on land with windmills. It was an important beginning, for, after all, sail ruled the sea for forty-eight centuries.

While Bronze Age men were taking giant strides forward in mechanics, a development vital to the spread of technology was taking place. Around 3500 B.C., in the Fertile Crescent kingdom of Sumer—roughly the country we know as Iraq— some inspired men were at work inventing writing. (Because Sumer produced nineteen types of beer, some say its entire populace must have been inspired.)

The first form of writing was picture, or ideographic, writing. Then, over the years, the pictures began to represent syllables instead of things. The final step, taken about 1,300 B.C. was the invention of an alphabet. With an alphabet, the spoken word could also be written. The written word is, of course, our most important tool for spreading knowledge.

AMERICAN MUSEUM OF NATURAL HISTORY
These Spanish cave drawings show archers hunting deer.

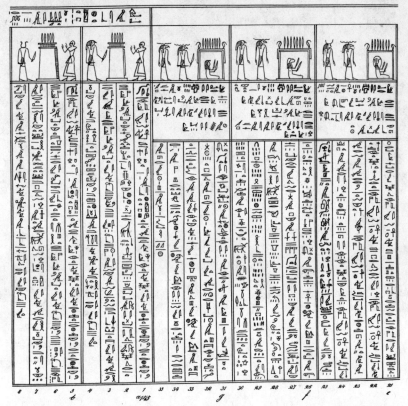

An example of Egyptian hieroglyphics.

As man stood on the threshold of the Christian Era, he had invented agriculture and conquered metal. He had made a healthy start towards harnessing water, the horse, and the wind—the only sources of energy for running his machines he would command for almost 2,000 years. In writing he had the necessary tool for spreading his knowledge throughout the world.

Moreover, without realizing it our Stone, Bronze, and Iron Age ancestors had invented the five basic mechanisms with which our present material world was built. Known as the

The impression of this cylinder seal gives the royal name and title of "Darius, the Great King" in Old Persian, Elamite, and Babylonian cuneiform.

"simple machines," they are the lever, the wheel and axle, the pulley, the screw, and the wedge, with its twin the inclined plane. These five simple machines, and these alone, make it possible for machinery to *move* and do the work we demand. In truth, without these gifts from our early ancestors we might still be living in caves.

Perhaps the first man to recognize the full importance of the simple machines, and certainly the first to describe their significance, was a Greek inventive genius. He was called Hero of Alexandria.

PART 2

5

HERO OF ALEXANDRIA

HERO was a Greek who was born in Alexandria sometime during the years the Egyptian seaport was a part of the Greek Empire. He is thought to have lived at about the same time as Christ. We can't be sure because we know nothing of his personal life, not even his birth date.

Knowing his birthplace does tell us one thing, though. He grew up in the shadow of the great lighthouse of Alexandria. Built in 280 B.C., it stood more than 250 feet high, and its polished metal reflecting mirrors, which picked up light from a wood fire, threw a beam that could be seen 35 miles at sea! The lighthouse was a spectacular engineering feat. It may well have given Hero his interest in all things mechanical.

Our only firsthand knowledge of Hero comes from his writings. They leave no doubt as to his inventive genius. The descriptions of the five simple machines, found in his three-volume *Mechanica,* make it clear that he was also a student of the principles of mechanics.

To understand the lever, the wheel and axle, the pulley, the screw, and the wedge and inclined plane, you must first understand something else. In mechanics, work is not something you do for a living. Instead, it is defined as a force—whether it be muscular strength or nuclear power—acting over a distance to overcome a resistance. The virtue of the simple machines is that they reduce the amount of force necessary to overcome a resistance. They thus give us what engineers call a "mechanical advantage."

For example, suppose you had to move a 120-pound steel bar from the ground onto a wheelbarrow whose bed is 1 foot above the ground. You haven't the strength to lift the bar; but if you lay a plank from the ground to the wheelbarrow, you will have an inclined plane. With the mechanical advantage it gives you, you can then do the job. If it's a 2-foot plank, a short steep plane, you'll have to exert a 60-pound force to roll the bar up the plank. With a 3-foot plank, a 40-pound effort is required. With a longer gently sloping 4-foot plank, a 30-pound push will overcome the bar's resistance.

In each instance, when you multiply the force you exert by the length of the plank, the sum is 120, the exact weight of the steel bar you couldn't lift. In terms of *work*, then, the result is always the same as it would have been had you been able to lift the bar. Notice that in using inclined planes your work grew easier as your planks grew longer. This illustrates the basic law of mechanics: A smaller effort over a longer distance does the same amount of work as a great effort over a short distance. Now you know why in mechanics work is considered a multiple of distance times the force used to overcome a resistance.

The lever offers another example of how the force-times-distance equation works. The simplest lever is a stout rod that is supported at some point along its length by a firm object known as a "fulcrum." Let's assume now that you have to move a 120-pound rock. With a strong pole and a cement block for a fulcrum, it can be done fairly easily.

Shove one end of the pole under the rock. To gain your mechanical advantage, place the cement block beneath the

pole one foot away from the rock. Now push down on the free
end of the pole, the end technically known as the "effort arm"
of a lever. If the effort arm extends 2 feet from the cement
block, or fulcrum, moving the 120-pound rock will require a 60-
pound effort on your part. If you have a 3-foot effort arm, a 40-
pound push will do. If the effort arm extends 6 feet from the
fulcrum, an easy 20-pound push will move the rock. Here
again, when you multiply the forces exerted by the length of
the effort arms, in each instance the sum—120 pounds—equals
the weight of the rock. Again, a smaller effort over a longer
distance does the same work as a great effort over a short distance.

Levers come in three types and are classified according to
the placement of the fulcrum. In the one just described the
fulcrum was placed *between* the effort arm and the resistance
to be overcome, the rock. Pump handles, pliers, scissors, crowbars, and oars are examples of this class of lever. In type two,
the fulcrum is located *ahead* of the resistance, at the forward
end of the effort arm. A simple example is a nutcracker. Another is a wheelbarrow, with its effort-arm handles and a wheel
for a fulcrum.

A power shovel is typical of the third kind of lever. Its fulcrum lies *behind* the resistance, at the rear end of the effort
arm. For that matter, whenever you fish, go to bat, or swing an
ax, your elbow is a type-three fulcrum. Your fishing rod, bat, or
ax handle is the effort arm that helps you hit a home run, land
a fish, or chop down a tree.

Turning to the wheel and axle, we find that force and distance are still related. Here the distances involved are the radius of the wheel and the radius of the axle. Thus a 10-inch
wheel on a 1-inch axle multiples force by 10, and, it follows, a
10-foot wheel on the same 1-inch axle multiples force by 120.

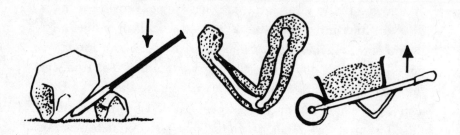

Three types of levers and their uses.

In addition, the mechanical advantage of the wheel and axle can be increased by combining geared wheels of different sizes —a matter of utmost importance in machinery.

If gear-wheel A, for instance, has ten times as many teeth as gear-wheel B, B will turn ten times faster than A when the teeth of the two wheels mesh. It is because of gear wheels that you can turn the blades of your mother's eggbeater with such speed and force. Notice, too, that the crank wheel of the egg beater is set at right angles to the gear wheel that drives the blades. This converts perpendicular force to horizontal force. This is a simple illustration of how engineers use gears to control the speed, power, and direction of the force wheels generate.

The wheel and axle is unquestionably the most versatile of the simple machines. It is used in thousands of different ways, ranging from the ferris wheel to the gyroscope, the bicycle, the selection dial on your TV set, and the doorknob. The list is so vast, in fact, that no one person could possibly name all the adaptations of the wheel-and-axle principle now in use.

In Hero's *Mechanica*, the pulley was described as a separate simple machine, and some people still agree. However, many modern mechanical engineers will argue that it is simply another variation of the wheel and axle. Their reasoning seems logical. A pulley is round, after all, and it does turn on an axle.

As you know, a single fixed pulley doesn't give you any mechanical advantage. It merely changes the direction of your effort. You pull down to lift up. Two or more pulleys have to be linked together before you gain an advantage. Then you can lift weights you couldn't budge with one pulley. By now you should be able to guess why. It is because the rope you pull on travels a greater distance through a series of connected pulleys than it does through a single pulley. Once more, it's a question of force times distance. This is why pulleys are used in series in weight-lifting machines like elevators, cranes, and hoists.

Primitive flint knives and fist axes were wedges because they had sloping sides. Since almost all cutting and piercing tools

The wheel and axle and its application.
Force on spokes of wheel is multiplied by 10.   *Axle 1"*
Gear wheel B turns 10 times as fast as gear A.   *Axle 10"*

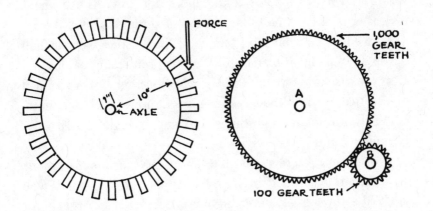

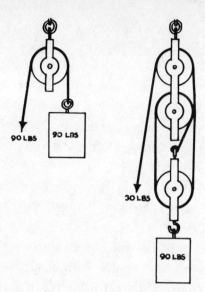

Increasing the number of pulleys increases the weight that can be lifted. 1) A single pulley only changes direction of forces. 2) With 3 pulleys in a block and tackle, 30 lbs. of force applied over a longer distance will lift 90 lbs.

have sides or points that slope, they, too, are members of the wedge family. It is an immense family that includes all chisels, knives, gangplows, hatchets, carpenter's planes, air hammers, needles, and their host of relatives. Yet, varied as they are, one rule holds for all wedges: the longer they are in relation to their thickness the easier it is for them to overcome resistance. It's a rule you've probably tested and found true. As you know, it's easier to drive a nail than a hatchet through a thick board.

All wedges do their job by moving. But a wedge cut in half becomes an inclined plane. It "works" by remaining motionless, as in the case of the plank and the wheelbarrow. Other inclined planes that work without moving are staircases, chutes, automobile ramps, railroad gradings, and sloping highways that cut through mountains.

In one sense a screw is nothing more than an inclined plane wound spirally around a central core, as you can see if you study the threads of a common screw. You could argue, too, that a screw shouldn't be called a simple machine, because it has to be turned by another simple machine: a lever like a screwdriver or the handle of a corkscrew or a vise.

Nevertheless, the screw is considered one of the simple machines. Like its partners, it can perform a wide variety of work. Screws fasten objects together. They grip them (in a vise), press them (in cider or wine presses), grind them (in meat and coffee grinders), and do any number of other jobs. Ship and plane propellers, for example, are able to "screw" their way through air and water only because their blades are pitched like a screw's threads. Even a boomerang makes use of the principle of the screw, because each of its ends is pitched on a different plane.

If a screw's circular, or rotary, motion is converted into straight-line motion, as it is in the jackscrew used to raise houses from their foundations and some automobile jacks, a screw can lift enormous weights. Here again there is an interplay between distance and force, with both the distance between the screw's threads and the length of the lever that turns it playing a role. Ordinarily, jackscrew threads are one-quarter of an inch apart. Turned with a 5-foot bar, a 40-pound effort will lift 30 tons one-quarter of an inch with each turn of the screw. With a short 1-foot bar, five times as much force is, of course, necessary—a back-breaking 200-pound push.

The wedge and the inclined plane may have been the earliest machines to be used by man. The hatchet applies the wedge principle. 25 lbs. of force exerted over a distance of 4 ft. will raise a 100 lb. cylinder 1 ft.

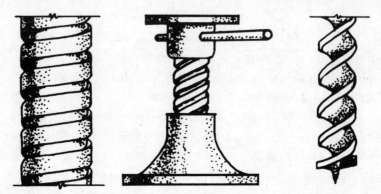

The screw principle applies to numerous useful machines.
Screw   Jackscrew   Drill

It is impossible to overstate the importance of the simple machines, because, directly or indirectly, they are involved in almost everything you do. They help produce the movies you see, the candy you eat, the books you read. You can't even take a drink of water from a tap without bringing into play the principles of the lever, the wheel and axle, and the screw, because those are the principles on which the parts that make up a water faucet are built.

A machine as simple as your bicycle has wheels. They are turned by a drive-pulley unit—the combination of the linked chain and the rear and pedal sprockets, which have wedge-shaped teeth. The handle bars are levers, and screws in the shape of threaded bolts hold the frame together. Another example is the typewriter on which these words were written. Screws help hold it together. Its type bars are levers. The type itself is wedgeshaped to give it a sharp striking face. The ribbon winds on wheels, or spools, and a pulley device moves the carriage.

In truth, every piece of machinery you use or can possibly name combines one or more of the simple machines whose importance Hero first recognized. But he did more than write about them. He also experimented with them, with amazing results. Among other things, he invented the following: an air gun, a fire engine with a force pump; a surveying instrument; a puppet theater run by falling weights; and a coin machine for the sale of sacred water in temples that worked on the same principle as our candy, stamp, and sandwich slot-machines.

These, however, were the least of Hero's triumphs. He also invented a machine for opening temple doors, and thereby became the father of automation. What he did was build a hollow, air-tight temple altar and placed a water-filled container beneath it. The container was fitted with two tubes. One opened into the altar's air space; the other led to an empty bucket. When a priest lit a fire on the altar the air inside it grew hot and, as heated air always does, expanded.

The only path of escape for the expanded air was the tube leading into the water container. When the air pushed into it, the water in the container was forced out through the tube leading to the bucket. When it was filled with water, the bucket sank of its own weight, pulling ropes that opened the temple doors with it. As you can see, once the altar fire was lit, Hero's machine *proceeded step-by-step through a pre-established pattern of performance*—which is the way modern engineers define one form of automation.

Hero next invented a wind machine for powering a temple organ. (Pipe organs were well known in the ancient world. Indeed, there was one in Jerusalem, fed by a huge bellows made of two elephants' hides, which could be heard a mile away.) The key feature of Hero's machine was a short stick that stuck out at a right angle from the axle of a wheel fitted with wind scoops. When the wind turned the wheel, the stick pressed down a lever. The lever, in turn, raised a piston, which sucked air into the organ. As the wheel continued around, the stick slipped past the lever and let the piston drop. With each revolution of the wheel the piston rose and fell, pumping a steady flow of air into the organ.

Hero's short stick sounds insignificant, but it was the first device to solve a basic problem in mechanics: how to convert a wheel's rotary motion into an up-and-down movement called reciprocating motion. Thus, Hero can also be credited with the invention of the *cam*, the name now given all parts that are attached to revolving shafts or axles to produce reciprocating motion. Today, cams are used in innumerable ways. They move the blades in electric razors, needles in sewing machines, and raise and lower the valves in the motor of your family car to mention a few examples.

Hero's best-remembered invention, however, was his *aeolipile*, named after the Greek god of the winds, Aeolus. It was a water-filled copper pot set on a tripod. Rising from the pot's lid were two arms—one of them hollow—which supported a hollow sphere that was free to rotate on a horizontal axle. Two small tubes stuck out of the sphere, bent at right angles, like the arms of a swastika. When the water in the pot was brought to a boil, steam flowed into the sphere through the hollow arm. Once the steam filled the sphere, it then shot out of the two bent tubes with a jetlike force that set the sphere spinning.

As the first steam-driven device the *aeolipile* was the undisputed father of the steam engine and the steam turbine. What's more, in building it Hero relied on a major law of physics, which wasn't formally recognized until an English physicist, Sir Isaac Newton, described it some 1,700 years later. The law states that every action is opposed by an equal reaction. It is the law of motion that accounts for the kick of a gun when a bullet is fired. It also explains the reaction of a toy balloon

Hero's aeolipile, the first reaction engine powered by steam.

when you blow it up and toss it in the air. The rush of air out of the balloon is what propels it forward.

Thus the *aeolipile* was also the first "reaction" machine. In reacting to the thrust of steam, it was set in motion by the same power principle that sends a jet plane winging through the air and a rocket soaring into the sky. Yet, in its day, the *aeolipile* was considered nothing more than a curiosity, a mere toy, and was soon forgotten!

Of all inventors, Hero was probably the most prophetic. His inventions hinted at things to come, world-changing things that were beyond even his fertile imagination: the ages of steam, and automation, and rocketry. But for hundreds of years the inventors that followed him could not take full advantage of his discoveries. They still had too much to learn about tools. Furthermore, it would be many centuries before his *aeolipile* would be remembered. Then, with the help of new technical skills, a practical steam engine could be made. With it, for the first time man would be able to build power into machines themselves. This would mark the beginning of what we call the Industrial Revolution—a revolution that still goes on.

PRELUDE TO REVOLUTION

FROM the age of Hero to the first rumblings of the Industrial Revolution, less than three centuries ago, progress in technology was highly uneven. While there were advances in many fields, others stood almost still. In at least one instance a step backward was taken.

The move back was in agriculture. One of Hero's countrymen invented a harvesting machine. It was a two-wheeled vehicle pushed by oxen, and having a comblike row of sharp teeth that cut grain from its stalks and collected it in a bin set between the wheels. The harvester could do the work of several men. But it never became popular and was eventually forgotten, for reasons soon to be made clear. As a result, for fifteen centuries men went on farming with basically the same plow and the same hand tools used in the Iron Age.

The history of an Egyptian monument illustrates how time stood still in some instances. Called an obelisk, it was 75 feet tall and weighed 327 tons. In Hero's time, Roman engineers transported it from Egypt to Rome with the help of levers and capstans, tugged and pushed at by an army of men and horses.

Fifteen hundred years later the obelisk was moved again, from a plaza in Rome to the square facing the great church of St. Peter's. How was it done? In almost exactly the same way: with capstans and levers and a straining army of 900 men and

140 horses. There was only one unusual difference. An executioner was on hand to behead any workman who shirked his duty.

The presence of the executioner proved one thing. A practice that went back to at least the building of the pyramids was drawing to an end: the use of slaves and forced labor. This practice explains in part why mankind was so slow in turning to mechanization after the five simple parts for building machinery became known.

In pagan antiquity, the nations around the eastern end of the Mediterranean rose to power by conquest, one by one, then fell when more powerful nations defeated them. At the height of their power, the victorious nations held captive thousands of soldiers taken prisoner in battle, all of them doomed to slavery. Should an emperor or his attendant noblemen ever be short of slaves, they could force the common people of their own country to do their work.

When King Cheops of Egypt decided to build the Great Pryamid at Gizeh, in 2575 B.C., he had no trouble finding 100,000 men to construct it. What's more, he kept his forced-labor gang at the same strength for the twenty years it took to build the pyramid. Once the Greeks became the rulers of the Near East, they, too, embraced slavery—the population of their capital, Athens, was at one point half slave.

Then Greece fell to the Romans, who in one campaign alone took 150,000 prisoners. During one period, when Rome's rulers were auctioning off as many as 10,000 prisoners a day, the city was served by 200,000 slaves. The famous Roman aqueducts and bridges were built by slaves. Through the use of slave labor, the Roman Empire became so crisscrossed with stone-paved highways that road maps had to be issued.

When Rome fell in A.D. 476, slavery went into decline,

largely because the spread of Christianity was leading people to the belief that slavery was immoral. Even so, a lesser form of slavery, called serfdom, lingered on for centuries. Serfs were common laborers, usually farm hands, who *went with* a piece of land. That is, if one feudal lord seized or purchased an estate from another, the people living on the land became the property of the new owner, to do with much as he pleased. In addition, kings retained their absolute power and could force their subjects to do any work a kingly whim decreed.

Thus, it was mainly because of slavery that the Roman harvester fell into disuse. Why bother to build a machine when you have slaves to do its work? It was because of slavery, too, that no executioner was needed when the obelisk was first moved. An executioner was necessary 1,500 years later, because then the work was done by serfs and common people at the order of their ruler. And by that time serfs and commoners were beginning to resist kings who, at times, treated them like slaves. So to keep their people in line, harsh rulers sometimes threatened them with troops and public executioners. Wiser kings, however, were beginning to do away with the worst aspects of serfdom. As their influence spread, all forms of enforced labor were gradually abandoned.

When the obelisk was erected in front of St. Peter's, the end of serfdom was already in sight. Though it was slow in coming, its end was one of the glories of the Middle Ages (the name given the period from the fall of Rome to the 1500's). As one historian points out, its end brought on the "founding for the first time of a complex civilization which rested not on the backs of sweating slaves or serfs but on non-human power."

Actually, Rome introduced the large-scale use of nonhuman power in the years just before her empire collapsed. Her military might had begun to decline, and she no longer owned enough slaves to grind all of the flour her populace needed. Yet, the people were clamoring for more and cheaper bread. To meet the demand, Roman engineers built a number of water-powered flour mills, which were probably the first large factories in history.

One of them, for example, was stepped down a hillside in such a manner that water from a river falls turned sixteen water wheels one after the other. The axle of each wheel was fitted with a wooden gear that meshed with a gear that turned a millstone. It was an astonishing mill, even by our standards. In a ten-hour day, it could grind 28 tons of flour, enough to make bread for 80,000 people!

In the Middle Ages, though, large factories were the rare exception, not the rule. In fact, not until the 1500's do we find another factory with an output measuring up to today's standards. It was a shipyard in Venice, Italy, called the Arsenal, and was Europe's largest industrial establishment in its day. The yard employed more than 1,000 skilled craftsmen, divided into small groups. Each group specialized in the manufacture of a single ship-part, like a mast or a rudder. Finished ships were put together by an assembly-line technic. In 1570, the Arsenal built one hundred galleys for a campaign against the Turks in the space of two months. In a demonstration for a visiting French king, a few years later, the yard launched and fitted out a warship in an hour!

For the most part, however, industry in the Middle Ages was confined to small factories, foundries, forges, and mills. Up to the twelfth century they were powered by water wheels. Then the windmill moved into Europe from the Near East; but windmills had their drawbacks. While they could supply power for machinery in regions where no running water was available, they were, of course, as unreliable as the wind itself.

The machines of the period usually operated in one of two ways. They were turned by meshed gears, like the Roman flour mills, or the axles of their water wheels and windmills were fitted with cams to convert rotary motion to up-and-down reciprocating motion.

Cammed axles were used mainly to operate drop hammers and trip hammers. The cams were like giant fingers sticking out of an axle. Each time an axle turned they lifted a hammer, then let it drop with a thud. The heavy hammers were used in mines to crush ore, in leather tanneries to crush bark, in foundries to forge and shape metal, and in textile mills to pound wool cloth in water to make it shrink.

When blast furnaces were invented in the sixteenth century and it finally became possible to melt and cast iron, cammed axles were used to pump the bellows that fed air to the large new furnaces. They were used in water-powered sawmills, too. But while cams could force a saw down, they couldn't reverse

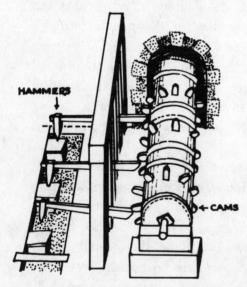

This foundry machine converted rotary motion from a waterwheel to up-and-down motion as the cams on the axle hit the hammer handles.

themselves and provide power for the upstroke. To complete the cycle an important new device was added.

It was a spring pole. One end was attached to the ceiling. The free end was connected to the saw. The cam drove the saw down against the pull of the spring pole. When the cam released the saw, the bent pole straightened, pulling the saw into the upstroke.

The spring pole built an entirely new reaction into machinery, and it was soon put to enormously important use in the lathe. A lathe is a device that spins an unfinished piece of wood, metal, or other material, while a cutting or shaping tool is pressed against the revolving surface of the material. Crude lathes were used in the Iron Age. Their operators had to turn them with one hand while applying the cutting tool to the workpiece with their other unsupported, and thus unsteady, hand. Inevitably their finished work was uneven. Today, we have lathes that cut screws, gears, crankshafts, and other machine parts to the ten-thousandths of an inch tolerance demanded by modern mass production.

The door to this incredible precision was opened in the Middle Ages, when turners wrapped a line from a spring pole around their lathes and connected it to a foot pedal. With this connection a worker could turn his workpiece at a constant speed with his foot; and with both hands free to control his cutting tools, he could use them with vastly greater skill and delicacy.

For the future of technology, the powered lathe was one of the two most important tools to come out of the Middle Ages. The second was the boring mill, which also developed into an unbelievably precise tool. Among its many current uses are the machining of cylinder walls and the boring of holes, threaded

A sixteenth-century cannon-boring mill powered by water.

or unthreaded and of every imaginable size and shape, to the fine tolerances that make assembly-line production possible.

The lathe and the boring mill are known as the Adam and Eve of the machine age because of the roles they played in starting it. Obviously, you can't build a machine until you shape its parts, which a lathe does, and you can seldom join moving parts without drilling holes in them. This is the boring mill's job.

The power-driven boring mill was the product of warfare. A cannon was fired in anger for the first time in the 1300's, probably in a battle between the English and the Scots. It and most other muzzle-loading smoothbore cannon of the Middle Ages were made by the *cire perdue* process, of cast bronze, brass, or iron. When their clay molds were broken and the clay cores removed from their barrels, the barrels had to be bored even smoother if they were to be at all accurate.

At first the smoothing was done by hand. By the 1500's arms makers had learned to do the job by power. To the axles of water wheels they attached horizontal bars with metal-cutting heads that precisely fitted the barrels of their cannon. Then the turning wheels did the work of reaming out the barrels. Ironically, from engines of destruction we got a tool that now serves us in countless peaceable ways.

There were other inventions in the Middle Ages, of course. To mention a few: trousers, soap, gunpowder, felt hats, compasses, buttons, clocks, and spinning wheels. As we've mentioned, it was also the period in which the blast furnace, horsecollar, horseshoe, tandem harness, and stirrup appeared.

It was in the Middle Ages, too, that the printing press with moveable type was introduced—an invention that led to an output of more books in fifty years than had been produced by hand in the preceding thousand years. For generations a German, Johann Gutenberg, was credited with this invention. As a result, many people still believe that the Gutenberg Bible of 1450 was the first book printed from moveable type. However, for years scholars have known that moveable type was in general use in Korea in the 1300's. There is a printed document dated 1397 in Korea's National Museum, in Seoul, to prove it. Credit for the invention of this immeasureably important tool for spreading knowledge must go to the Far East.

The Middle Ages were followed by the Renaissance. Lasting until the end of the 1600's, the Renaissance is considered the bridge between medieval and modern times and is chiefly remembered for its great art and architecture. Many people also believe it produced a remarkable array of machinery. This is a false belief, created largely by the notebooks of the Renaissance's greatest figure, Leonardo da Vinci.

Da Vinci's genius was boundless. He was a great painter, sculptor, scientist, engineer, architect, and mechanic, who recorded his wide-ranging ideas in notebooks that are now world-famous. In them, among other things, his detailed drawings showed how alarm clocks, parachutes, pile drivers, diving suits, and submarines might be made. He drew the first ball bearing and blueprinted the chain drive we now use on bicycles and other machines. He designed a flying machine; several hoists, cranes, and pumps; a helicopter; and machines for making coins, screws, cloth, rope, and for grinding a lens. The list is almost endless.

What we fail to realize, though, is that few of his inventions ever got off the drawing board. Most of them remained hidden in his notebooks, which he kept so private they had little influence on the technology of his day. The world at large didn't learn of them until 278 years after his death. In 1797, Napoleon found a bundle of the notebooks in the loot of his Italian campaign and made them public. Only then did people learn that as a *designer* of machinery da Vinci was four centuries ahead of his time.

Da Vinci's art works were masterpieces. As an engineer and architect, he designed and built superb military fortifications, public buildings, and canals. As a scientist, he broadened man's knowledge with his experiments. But as an inventor his genius was largely confined to paper. Thus, Renaissance technology cannot properly be judged on the basis of his prophetic drawings of things to come. Indeed, in da Vinci's time "there were no major inventions" in the opinion of one widely accepted historian. The air pump, the screw-cutting lathe, the knitting machine, the rifle, and the adding machine are about the only Renaissance tools that win mention in historical surveys of inventions.

Yet, paradoxically, it was the man of the Renaissance who made the Industrial Revolution possible. But it was not the Renaissance mechanic or engineer. It was the scientist of the Renaissance. Scientists were the truly remarkable inventors of the era. In devising such scientific instruments as the telescope, the microscope, the thermometer, and the barometer, among

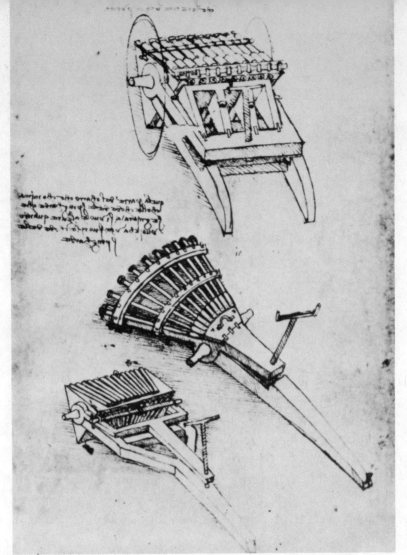

Leonardo da Vinci's sketches for machine guns.

others, they actually created modern science. Their laboratory experiments led to most of the engineering achievements of the Industrial Revolution. This was particularly true of the steam engine, the keystone of the entire Revolution.

What triggered the development of the steam engine was the problem of mine drainage. In the 1660's there were 600-foot mine shafts. For reasons no one understood, suction pumps could raise water no more than 30 feet. This made pumping water from mines so complicated that an Italian prince asked some scientists to study the matter. In 1664, a physicist named Evangelista Torricelli discovered that at sea level the pressure of the atmosphere raised a column of mercury 30 inches. Because of the mercury's greater weight, this corresponded to a 30-foot column of water. Here was the first indication that the weight of air was responsible for the suction pump's inability to raise water more than 30 feet.

A Dutch scientist named Otto von Guericke provided additional proof of the immense force of atmospheric pressure. He joined together two close-fitting hemispheres, forming a hollow sphere about twice the size of a basketball. Then he drew all of the air out of the sphere with a suction pump. This created a vacuum. There was no air pressure left inside the sphere to offset the air pressure outside it. The outside atmospheric pressure pressed the two hemispheres together with such force that two teams of eight powerful horses couldn't pull them apart! Since atmospheric pressure is 14 pounds per square inch, it would have taken a pull of several tons to overcome the tremendous weight of air pressing on the surface of the two hemispheres.

In a second experiment, more closely related to the steam engine, Von Guericke created a vacuum beneath a large piston set in a cylinder. When he did this, 50 men couldn't hold the piston in place. Despite their combined effort, atmospheric pressure forced the piston down into the cylinder. Both experiments showed that if some way could be found to repeatedly create a vacuum, the force of atmospheric pressure could be put to work.

French scientist Denis Papin found the way. He made a

Otto von Guericke's demonstration of air pressure with the Magde-burg hemispheres. From a copper engraving in 1672.

laboratory study of steam pressure. It is thought that he became interested in steam through reading the description of the *aeolipile* in Hero's *Mechanica,* which after a lapse of fifteen centuries had been republished in the 1600's, but it can't be proved. In any event, in 1690, Papin wrote the following his-oric words, which describe the theory underlying all early steam engines:

> *A small quantity of water turned into steam by heat has an elastic force like that of air. But upon being cooled it again resolves into water, so that no trace of the elastic*

force remains. I conclude that machines could be con-
structed wherein water, by the help of heat and at little
cost, could produce a perfect vacuum.

It wasn't known then that a quart of water boils into 1,700 quarts of steam! But Papin had discovered, in principle, that if you condense 1,700 quarts of steam back to one quart of water you do, indeed, create a nearly perfect vacuum. Furthermore, he'd found a way to create a vacuum repeatedly. To prove his theory, he poured water into a 2½-inch-wide cylinder fitted with a piston; then he boiled the water. The steam forced the piston up. When he doused the cylinder in cold water the steam condensed and formed a vacuum. Then atmospheric pressure forced the piston down. Papin's next step was to connect one end of a rod to the piston, the other end to a water-filled bucket. When alternate heating and cooling drove the piston up and down, the bucket also rose and fell.

Papin's experiment showed how a combination of steam and atmospheric pressure could be put to work for man. Within eight years a huge over-sized adaptation of his laboratory device was actually pumping water from a mine. Called "The Miner's Friend," it was built by Thomas Savery—a man about whom we know little except that he owed his patent on an "engine to raise water by fire" more to Papin's research than his own inventiveness.

The Miner's Friend was a crude, clumsy, impractical machine, soon to be replaced by better ones; but it *was* the first steam engine ever put to use. A turning point in history was reached when this steam engine began pumping water out of a mine from a depth of a couple of hundred feet in 1698. That was the moment that ushered in the age of steam, the moment the prelude ended and the Industrial Revolution began.

PART 3

7

FULL STEAM AHEAD

THE FIRST world's fair in history was held in London, England, in 1851. Called "A Great Exhibition of the Works of Industry of All Nations," its purpose was to display the great variety of power-driven machinery produced in the century and a half since The Miner's Friend began chugging. The exhibition was held in the Crystal Palace, an iron-and-glass building one-third of a mile long, which in itself was an engineering marvel. To those who visited the Crystal Palace, it was clear that the Industrial Revolution was in full swing and that England was the workshop of the world.

England was, in fact, the cradle of the Industrial Revolution and for many years the manufacturing center of the world, for good reasons. The first stage of the revolution is usually called the Age of Steam. The steam engine was invented in England. Englishmen transformed it from a mere mine-pumping device to a machine for mechanizing industry. Steam engines burn vast quantities of fuel, and England had huge coal deposits. Industry's basic need is iron and steel, and the country had equally large deposits of iron ore. England, then, had the necessary raw materials to build the first industrial society, and as the maker of the first steam engines, also had a head start on the rest of the world.

With surprising speed, steam changed England from a pri-

marily agricultural country to an industrial country. When The
Miner's Friend began pumping, for example, England was already mining five times as much coal as the rest of the world: 3
million tons a year. When the great exhibition opened, her
output had jumped to 60 million tons annually—and yet she
was having trouble keeping up with her fast-growing industrial
needs.

Her foundries were producing half of the world's supply of
finished iron. She had more than double the combined textile
manufacturing capacity of the United States and France, her
closest competitors. She had steam locomotives puffing over
6,600 miles of rail. She could boast that the Cunard Line—the
first steamship company to establish a regular transatlantic
service—had begun operating twenty years before the opening
of the Crystal Palace. Although England was being challenged
by the United States and many European countries, by 1851
the Industrial Revolution had made her the world's richest
manufacturing nation.

However, the Industrial Revolution brought England more
than wealth. As it did in every country it touched, it brought
about the greatest social and economic changes in history, and
altered the lives of millions of people.

When it began, most people lived in farm areas, and towns
served chiefly as market centers for farmers. This changed because the Revolution completely erased the medieval system of
farming. It also moved industry from the cottage or the small
mill nestled at the edge of a stream, where each craftsman had
been his own manufacturer, into the factory. Large three- and
four-story factories were built to house huge boilers and massive steam-powered machines. These factories employed so
many laborers—half a million in England's cotton mills alone
—that as often as not they transformed quiet country towns

into large manufacturing cities. With the growth of the factory system, trade increased. As a result, more roads and canals had to be built. Then the railroad and the steamship extended the revolution to transportation.

As for the people, millions left the farms to take jobs in factories. The peasant and yeoman gave way to the laborer, the feudal lord to the manufacturer and merchant. A middle class emerged and quickly grew in size. As the influence and power of the middle class gradually spread, the ruling class was forced to give up most of its privileges. This made for a more democratic way of life and brought the common man richer opportunities than he'd ever before enjoyed. Thus, the Age of Steam increased man's material well-being and also revolutionized his manner of living.

Obviously such a profound change wasn't due to steam alone. Other factors were involved. Yet, the steam engine was undeniably the fuse that set off the revolution. The single most important figure in the Age of Steam was a Scotsman named James Watt.

Watt was the creator of the first true steam engine, which operated on steam alone without relying on atmospheric pressure to drive its piston down. He did it with what has been called the "most important invention ever applied to the steam engine, without which the Industrial Revolution might never have reached full tide."

Bear in mind that Watt didn't invent a new engine. He improved an existing one. Only rarely since the 1700's has any one man been able to take full credit for a major advance in technology. More often, advances have been made by a succession of inventors, improving or adapting devices already in existence.

This was already true in 1757, when an English engineer

wrote, "Almost every Master Manufacturer hath a new invention of his own, or is daily improving on those of others." It was even truer when the Crystal Palace opened. By 1851, for example, the locomotives thundering across the English countryside, frightening cattle and startling farmhands, bore no resemblance to the first locomotive invented by Richard Trevithick in 1804. They had been improved beyond recognition by several inventors.

The same was true of the Cunard Line's steamships. They ran on the same basic principle as the *Clermont*, in which Robert Fulton steamed up the Hudson River in 1807. There the resemblance stopped due to alterations made by many inventors. Today, of course, tens of thousands of inventions are patented each year. Yet it is always front-page news when one of them works on an entirely new principle.

James Watt won fame not by discovering a new principle but by asking himself and then answering a simple question: Why must the cylinder of a steam engine be cooled off after each piston stroke?

In Papin's atmospheric engine, you may remember, to force the piston up, water in the cylinder had to be heated until it expanded and became steam. Then the cylinder had to be cooled to condense the steam and form a vacuum. Atmospheric pressure then forced the piston down. The Miner's Friend operated on Papin's principle, as did the slightly improved steam engine that replaced it in 1712. Both were highly inefficient and expensive to operate. When you have to heat a cylinder and then chill it to get a single piston stroke, a lot of time and energy are wasted. Also, the continual reheating burns up a lot of coal unnecessarily.

The genius of Watt's idea lay in its simple logic. He built an engine that would run without pause, because he devised a

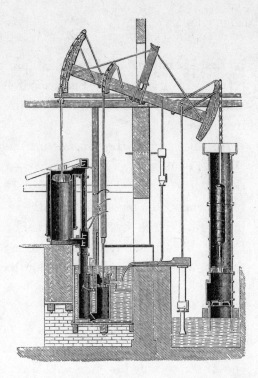

James Watt's single-acting pumping engine for mines.

way to keep its cylinder hot all the time. He cooled the steam in a separate tank, or condenser, rather than in the cylinder itself.

Furthermore, he built a double-action engine. He saw no reason to rely on atmospheric pressure when steam could be used to drive a piston down as well as up and with much greater force. With his cylinder always hot, he could inject steam into it through valves located above as well as beneath the piston head. When steam from the top valve forced the piston down, steam that had powered the upstroke was pushed into the condenser through an outlet valve. When the down-stroke ended, it tripped a valve that let steam into the bottom of the cylinder. This steam pushed the piston up, while the steam that had powered the downstroke escaped into the con-denser through an overhead outlet valve.

There was so little lost motion in the Watt engine that even his first operational model worked four times faster than atmospheric-pressure engines. Because of its double-action, it was also twice as powerful. It got three times as much work out of a ton of coal.

However, as in the air-pressure engines, a key feature of Watt's invention was a rocking bar—a wooden crossbeam like the balance arm of a pair of scales. The piston was connected to one end of the crossbeam and the up-and-down action of the piston made the free end of the beam move like a pump handle. Unfortunately, it was a motion suitable for little other than pumping. The wheels of industry have to *turn,* so what was badly needed was a rotary-motion engine.

Watt licked this problem too. It took him five years, but the method he devised is still used in principle in most of the world's engines. He added a perpendicular drive rod to the free end of the rocking bar, and with a set of gears he coupled the rod to the drive shaft, or axle, of a flywheel. The coupling of a piston-powered drive rod to a rotating drive shaft turned the flywheel.

Watt now had a rotary engine that could turn almost any piece of machinery. All that was needed was a drive belt (like the belt that turns the fan under the hood of your family car) that would connect his spinning flywheel to the machine in question. In addition, his engines were the most powerful available, and they could be installed anywhere. This meant that industry could, for the first time, build factories wherever it wanted to, not just on the banks of rivers swift enough to turn water wheels.

It is easy to see why Watt is considered the key figure in the Age of Steam, and why for many years engines based on his design provided most of the power for the factories of the Industrial Revolution.

Watt could never have built a practical and workable engine had it not been for the genius of a little-known man. He was John Wilkinson, an eccentric toolmaker and foundry owner who was so enthusiastic about cast iron that he left orders that on his death he was to be buried in a cast-iron coffin beneath a cast-iron tombstone, after funeral services held in a cast-iron chapel with a cast-iron altar—all of his own making. It was Wilkinson who made the tool that made Watt's engine usable.

Watt began work on his engine in 1765 and spent four unsuccessful years trying to perfect it. His main problem was the cylinder. No one could cast a steam-tight cylinder for him. Nor could he find a boring machine that could cut a reasonably precise diameter the full length of a cylinder. Consequently, all of the many piston-cylinder combinations he tried fitted so loosely that large quantities of steam escaped between the cylinder walls and the pistons. The great loss of steam pressure offset the improved design of his engine. As a result, his early experimental models were only slightly more efficient than the atmospheric-pressure engines they were meant to replace.

In 1769, Watt took his problem to one of England's leading engineers, only to be told, "Neither tools nor workmen exist that can manufacture so complex a machine with sufficient precision." Completely discouraged, he gave up his experiments until he met Wilkinson in 1774. Wilkinson had just invented a new boring mill for reaming out the cannon he had manufactured. It was the first ever built that could hold a cutting tool firmly in place and move it along a line so straight and true that it machined the full length of a cannon bore with accuracy and precision.

Wilkinson saw the full possibilities of Watt's engine at once. He volunteered to try using his boring mill to make the steam-tight cylinders Watt needed. The experiment was a complete success. The borer did the job. The Watt engine was finally perfected. The first one to go into operation was installed in John Wilkinson's foundry.

In its own way, Wilkinson's boring mill was as important as Watt's engine. Because of its then unmatched precision, it became the first member of the great family of machines that make other machines. Technically known as "machine tools," they are the foundation stones of present-day industry because they make the machinery that makes every single product we use: autos, books, toys, rockets, food, ships, fishing rods, chewing gum—everything. Think of the endless number of manufactured objects you use from the time you get up until you go to bed. From the shoes you put on to the pillow beneath your head, they were all made by machinery that was made by machine tools.

Machine tools are power-driven devices that carve, grind, cut, drill, press, and shave metal into parts that can be assembled into other machines. Basically, they are only six in number. They are:

(1) Boring mills and drills that make smooth, threaded, or tapered holes.

(2) Lathes that hold cutting tools against spinning cylinders of rough metal and whittle them into any shape a tool designer asks for.

(3) Planers that shave the flat and parallel surfaces necessary to all machinery in much the same way a carpenter's plane shaves the surface of wood.

(4) Milling machines whose rotating cutting tools have multiple cutting edges. The cutting tools, are in effect, continuously moving chisels that chip metal into special shapes in a single operation.

(5) Shears and presses that slice or bend metal into any shape or form.

(6) Grinding machines that give a metal part its final required smoothness, contour, or dimension, with a precision measured in terms of one-ten-thousandth of an inch.

The capability and versatility of these machines today is close to miraculous. Yet, it is worth remembering that they perform only the same basic operations as the simple instruments in the tool kit of Stone Age man. They are, after all, only tools that grind, cut, pierce, scrape, and hammer, just as his did. The real difference is that metal parts have replaced man's hands, arms, and body, and mechanical power, his muscle. Therein may lie the true miracle of machine tools. They and the tools they make have taken the heavy labor from men's backs and placed it on the tireless back of the machine.

THE HORSELESS AGE

For the first 150 years of the Industrial Revolution, British engineers were the world's best. Among their major inventions were the steam engine, the finest known textile-manufacturing machinery, the locomotive, and all of the basic machine tools. Their supremacy was so great that for a time piracy of patented English machinery was an organized business.

The first successful cotton mill in the United States, for instance, was based on a textile spinning machine whose plans were smuggled out of England in 1789. In the early 1800's, too, there was a factory in Belgium that did nothing but copy English machinery, without the patent holder's permission. According to an official British report, the factory could reproduce new inventions "ten days after they came out."

The great exhibition of 1851, however, marked the end of England's leadership. Thereafter, American and European inventors frequently led their British rivals. English toolmakers had nothing to do with the invention that probably changed our way of life more than any other single product of the Industrial Revolution. This was the internal-combustion engine, which led to the automobile.

It may surprise you to learn that Europe, not the United States, was the original home of the motor car. In Paris, for example, in 1900, cars were so common they had all but driven

horses off the city's main avenues. Yet, in America the automobile was still considered a smelly, noisy, rich man's toy,
which should perhaps be outlawed because it frightened
horses. Most Americans also had the feeling that automobiling
was both snobbish and sissified, like two other new fads, smok-
ing cigarettes and wearing wristwatches. This feeling was so
widespread that it actually led Theodore Roosevelt to give up
automobiling. In 1905, he wrote that he'd taken but two "auto
rides" during his presidency and would take no more, because
they created bad publicity and might cost him votes.

The average American's distrust of the automobile didn't
begin to fade until 1908, when Henry Ford introduced his first
car, which was nicknamed the "tin lizzie." In the next twenty
years, as mass-production methods dropped the car's price
from 825 to 260 dollars, an amazing 15 million tin lizzies were
sold. It was this car that put America on wheels and revolutionized our way of life. But the motor that made the lizzie run
was born in Europe.

The first vehicle designed to travel on roads was a weird
steam-driven three-wheeled carriage. Its boiler stuck so far out
over the single front wheel that it was said to look like "a small
factory trying to go somewhere on a wheelbarrow." The vehicle was built in 1769 by a Frenchman named Nicolas Joseph
Cugnot. He could travel up to 4 miles an hour in it *if* he
stopped every half mile or so to build up steam. It may be,
though, that Cognot's chief claim to fame rests in his having
been thrown into jail for driving his horseless carriage into a
stone wall. This made him the world's first-known traffic
violator!

Cugnot's automobile—if it can be called that—was impractical from the start because of its steam, or external-combustion,
engine. In external-combustion engines the fuel is burned out-

side, rather than inside, an engine's cylinder. All such engines need furnaces and large boilers to build up the steam they feed their cylinders. They must also have chimneys or smokestacks to carry off the smoke from their burning fuel. By their very nature steam engines require a lot of space.

It's true, external-combustion engines were practical for the factories of the Industrial Revolution. In reduced size, they were, for a while, also suitable for locomotives and steamships —though the engines and coal bunkers of the first Cunard liners so filled their hulls that they had no room for freight and could carry only passengers and mail.

For the automobile and for things to come, like the airplane, power lawnmower, outboard motor, and thousands of other present-day machines, the external-combustion engine was useless. What was needed was a much smaller engine. It had to be one that could be started and stopped at will, without waiting to build up a head of steam. And one that burned very little fuel, compared to the tons of coal a steam engine used.

All of these needs were recognized by the men who first tried to build small motors. They knew, too, that to reach their goal they had to develop an internal-combustion engine—one that burned fuel inside the piston-cylinder unit. The logical way to do away with the bulkiest parts of the steam engine—its furnace and boiler—was to make the cylinder take over their work.

Finding a suitable fuel was a problem that haunted every pioneer of the internal-combustion engine. One man built an engine in which the piston was driven by exploding gunpowder inside the cylinder, but it was too dangerous to use. He was followed, in 1807, by the Niepces, two French brothers who designed a motor that was safe, but their fuel was made from, of all things, a mosslike plant of the *Lycopodium* family! When

it was dried and pulverized the strange plant had an explosive
quality that made it useful to fireworks manufacturers. But
there just wasn't enough of the moss around to turn more than
a few car wheels.

The first sensible advance came in 1860, when the French
inventor Etienne Lenoir tried natural gas, until then used only
for cooking and lighting, as a fuel. He built what is called a
"double-cycle" internal-combustion engine. That is, its fuel was
exploded first at one end of the cylinder, then the other. The
explosions drove the piston back and forth, and a rod connected to the piston turned a flywheel.

Although Lenoir's invention marked the beginning of the
end of old-fashioned steam power it didn't win much attention.
To dramatize it, the inventor attached his engine to a carriage
and went thundering through the streets of Paris at 4 miles per
hour. It was the first hint of the automobile age to come, but
his fellow citizens were still unimpressed. Lenoir's engine ran
with an ear-splitting roar they didn't like. Further, it broke
down and had to be repaired too often to attract buyers.

The internal-combustion engine got its biggest boost, oddly
enough, from a book published in 1862. It was written by a
French scientist who worked out his entire theory in his mind,
without going near a machine shop. The man was Alphonse
beau de Rochas. What he had mentally pictured, then described in his book was an engine with a "four-stroke" cycle. To
this day most internal-combustion engines operate on four-
stroke cycles. The four strokes are:

(1) *Intake*—the piston moves down, sucking a mixture of
air and fuel from the carburetor into the cylinder. (2)
Compression—the fuel-intake valve closes and the piston
moves back up, tightly compressing the fuel vapor. (3)

Explosion—the exploding fuel drives the piston down, and a connecting rod changes the piston's straight-line motion into the crankshaft's rotary motion. This is the power stroke. (4) *Exhaust*—as the piston moves up again, an exhaust valve opens and the used gases are pushed out of the cylinder, clearing it for the first, or intake, stroke of the next cycle.

In a modern car the explosions in its six or eight cylinders don't go off all at once. They go off one after the other, in sequence, so that one cylinder is always on the power stroke. At fifty miles an hour there are about 100 explosions inside the engine every second! The intake and exhaust valves in each cylinder open and shut about 20 times a second.

Inspired by de Rochas' book, a self-educated German mechanic, N.A. Otto, built the first four-cycle engine in 1876. Like Lenoir's two-cycle motor, it ran on natural gas. But it used only half the fuel and ran twice as fast. Otto, however, designed his

The diagrams show the sequence of four strokes in the most common type of internal-combustion engine. 1) Intake; 2) Compression; 3) Power; 4) Exhaust.

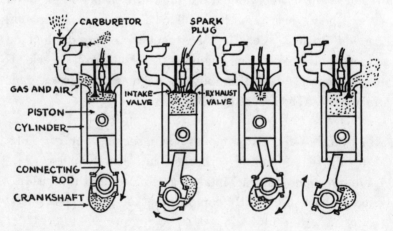

engine as a power plant for small industries that couldn't afford steam. In this role, it proved so successful that it was soon being used by 50,000 factories the world over.

The man who put the Otto engine on the road was another German, Karl Benz. His first car, a three-wheeled vehicle, appeared on the streets of Munich in 1885. Eight years later he put out an improved four-wheeled model, which he sold by the hundreds in the years before the century ended.

The Benz car was the first to run on gasoline, and this may have saved the infant oil industry of his day. It was a difficult time for oil refiners. They were interested only in producing kerosene to light the world's lamps, and gas lights were beginning to give them stiff competition. As for gasoline, they considered it a worse than useless by-product of the kerosene refining process because it was a dangerous fire hazard. In fact, before Benz found a use for it, they threw their gasoline away!

Benz also introduced two other features of the automobile that have since become standard. One was the radiator and water-cooling system that keeps the engine from overheating. The second was the electric ignition system that sparks the fuel in the cylinders. So it is easy to understand why Karl Benz is known to history as the "father of the automobile." What's more, he founded the world's largest single industry, the manufacture and sale of automobiles. When he sold the first Benz, a car that could travel a bumpy road at 11 miles per hour, he set in motion all the wheels that have carried us past the tin lizzie to the Cadillac and the Rolls Royce.

A short ten years after Benz sold his first car, the internal-combustion engine gave man something he had dreamed of for centuries: wings. The wings with which Wilbur and Orville Wright, in 1903, made the first airplane flight at Kitty Hawk, North Carolina, were, of course, feeble and untrust-

A Karl Benz motor car of 1888.

worthy. As we all know, though, they have since been so improved that man can now fly much faster and soar to far greater heights than the birds.

Today, of course, we have the jet engine pushing planes through the air faster than the speed of sound. It works, you may remember, on the same simple principle as Hero's spinning toy, the *aeolipile*. But the motor that powered the Wright brothers' plane, as well as most other planes during the first half of our century, scarcely differed from the one Karl Benz used. It was a four-cycle engine sparked by electricity. For that matter, so are the great majority of our present-day internal-combustion engines. You may be surprised to learn that there is nothing in any of them that would greatly startle either an automotive or an electrical engineer of the last century.

9

FROGS' LEGS
AND A COMPASS NEEDLE

SINCE it is hard to imagine how any gasoline internal-combustion engine could run without the aid of an electrical ignition system, the saga of that engine is, of course, linked to the story of electricity. This story begins before the time of Christ. Its end—if there is one—is not in sight.

The early Greeks were the first to puzzle over electricity, and small wonder, since there are things about it that still puzzle us. The Greeks were particularly mystified by amber. Amber is a hardened yellow resin from prehistoric pines that has long been used in jewelry. When a Greek jewelry maker polished amber with a dry cloth, he found that strange things happened. A tiny blue flame might leap from the amber to his outstretched fingers. The amber might also pull metallic filings to its surface and hold them there with a "magical" force.

Today, of course, we know that when you polish anything there is friction. We have learned that friction between *any* two materials generates electricity, though usually in such tiny quantities that it can be detected only by the most delicate scientific instruments. Amber, however, is a material in which friction, or rubbing, generates an unusually strong electrical charge. This is why the Greeks could see it spark. Because *every* electrical charge is surrounded by a magnetic field, when amber is rubbed hard enough to become electrified it also temporarily becomes a magnet. This is why it attracted metal filings, to the Greeks' amazement.

Have you ever scuffed your feet across a carpet, then received a shock when you touched a metal doorknob? If you have, you have generated electricity by friction. How you did it can be described; though like many of nature's miracles, the "how" isn't easily understood.

Electricity consists of invisible particles called "electrons." Electrons are present in every atom. As you know, everything in the world—this book, a rug, a doorknob, you yourself—is made up of atoms. There is an electrical charge, or a supply of electrons, in everything. It is the nature of electrons to be in constant motion. When they move slowly you can't feel them, but you know it when they move rapidly.

When you scuff across a carpet friction loosens some of the carpet's electrons, and they cling to you. You don't notice them because, for the moment, they are in slow motion. When you touch the doorknob, though, you become aware of them, for the extra electrons rush out of your body into the knob with lightning speed. And you get a shock!

The first scientists to experiment with electricity couldn't find a way to collect electrons and put them to use. In 1745, a professor at the University of Leyden, Holland, finally discovered one way to do it. He filled a glass jar with water. Then he dangled one end of an iron chain in the water and connected the other end to the spinning metal disk of a friction machine. When the machine stopped turning he touched the chain to see if any electricity had been stored in the jar—and got a shock that knocked him to the floor. He had invented the first electrical collector, or condenser.

News of the "Leyden Jar" spread and similar experiments were soon repeated throughout Europe. Leyden Jars become a fad, with people standing in line to be shocked by them. At the French Court, 180 guardsmen joined hands and were sent leaping into the air when the first in line touched a Leyden Jar. On another occasion, a highly charged jar bowled over 700 monks who had coupled hands to test this strange new power.

Although electricity was used in the popular show of the day, it was of no value otherwise. The Leyden Jar held static electricity, which is electricity at rest. Furthermore, its electrical discharge, though dramatic, was soon spent. If mankind was ever to benefit from electricity, a new type had to be found, one that was not static but active enough to flow through a wire, like water through a pipe. Only with a steady *current* of this new source of energy could the electrical miracles that we take for granted today be achieved.

Happily, the fact that electricity *could* flow was eventually discovered, though only by accident. An eighteenth-century Italian scientist, Luigi Galvani, quite by chance hung the legs of some freshly killed frogs on a copper hook attached to an iron bar. The legs, to his surprise began to twitch. Galvani thought some mysterious animal energy still remained in the legs. Another Italian, Alessandro Volta, disagreed. He suspected that the twitching was caused by electricity chemically produced by the combination of two different metals acted upon by the moisture in the flesh of the frogs' legs.

To test his theory Volta built what turned out to be the first electric battery. He built it of stacks of copper and zinc disks separated by cloth pads soaked with acid. The action of the acid on the metals released a steady stream of electrons. More important, the electrons flowed into the two wires connected to the opposite ends of the battery. Volta had produced the first current of electricity.

Volta opened the door to the warehouse of batteries we have

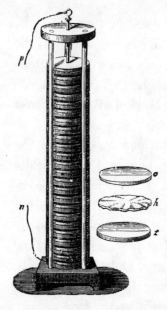

Alessandro Volta's first battery, built in 1800. Called the voltaic pile, it made use of the tiny flow of electrons which occurred when two different metals came in contact. Brine-soaked cloth acted as a conductor between the plates.

today. While batteries can create electrical currents by chemical action, however, they can't produce currents strong enough for most modern needs. For these a generator, or dynamo, is needed. The world owes an immense debt to Michael Faraday, an English scientist, for his discovery of the principle of the generator.

When a compass needle is placed under a live wire it no longer points north to the earth's magnetic pole. It points in another direction, at right angles to the wire. This is because the magnetic field set up by the electricity in the wire is stronger than the magnetic force of the pole. Toying with a compass and wire one day in 1831, Faraday got an inspiration. If electricity could create magnetism, he told himself, it was logical to assume that magnetism could in turn produce electricity.

He connected a coil of copper wire to a meter that measured the flow of an electric current. Then he placed a magnet near the coiled wire. The meter's pointer moved! The closer the magnet was to the coil the more the pointer moved. Faraday was right. Magnetism could produce electricity.

Next, Faraday mounted his coil of wire on an axle and placed it between the two ends, or poles, of an ordinary horse-shoe-shaped magnet. When the coil was spun so that it cut through the magnet's magnetic field, it generated an electric current strong enough to give Faraday a considerable shock.

Faraday's device was the first generator. It is Faraday's generator alone that has placed at our command the silent, unseen source of power that serves us in so many ways at the flick of a switch. While a generator in a powerhouse today looks vastly complicated, it is really nothing more than a modern version of Faraday's original model. On a smaller scale, the same is true of an automobile generator. Within each a coil of wire is spinning around inside powerful magnets, producing a steady flow of electricity. It's that simple, mechanically. But understanding the principle involved is more difficult. No one really knows exactly *why* the union of a wire coil and a magnet produces a flow of electricity.

The many almost unbelievable things electricity can do are too well known to repeat. One thing worth mentioning, though, is an amazing discovery made in recent years. It has been found that *every* living creature—you, an elephant, a mosquito—is in a very real sense an electrical system.

It may surprise you to learn that you are closely related to many of our electronic instruments. Every one of your nerve cells—the building blocks of your nerve-brain network—is electrically charged. Connected to a device for measuring electricity, the oscilloscope, all nerve cells discharge electricity in amounts that can be easily read. Nerve fibers, or groups of cells, serve you in much the same way wire circuits serve an electrical engineer.

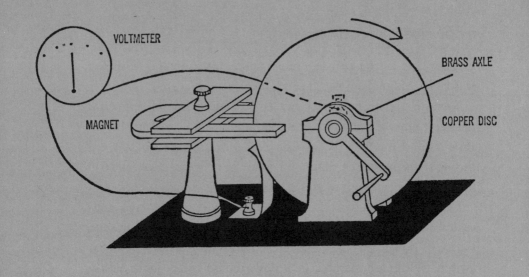

Faraday's dynamo used a rotating copper disc which passed through the lines of force of a magnet, inducing a current which registered on a voltmeter.

Have you ever stopped to think that your only "connection" with the outside world is through your sense organs, your eyes and ears and your sense of smell, taste, and touch? To an electronics expert your sense organs are "transducers," which is what instruments that change one form of energy into another are called. Microphones and TV cameras, for example, are transducers. A microphone changes sound waves into electrical signals, which are carried to a loudspeaker and converted back into sounds. A TV camera changes an image into electrical signals, which your receiving set converts back into a picture.

In the same way, the "transducing" nerve fibers in your ear convert a cry for help into electrical pulses that travel over the "wiring" of your nervous system to your brain at a speed of more than 400 feet a second. The brain decodes the signal, then sends an answering electrical-pulse message to your legs, where you change it into muscular energy when you start running in the direction of the cry. When you put your hand on a hot stove, nerve cells rush an electrical signal to your brain. In a flash the brain sends an order back over your nerve circuit, directing you to jerk your hand away from the heat. To move your hand, though, you have to convert the brain's electrical energy into muscular action.

Electronic engineers are now building mechanical transducers that do much the same work as our sense organs. They have developed extremely sensitive "eyes" and "ears," even an artificial "nose" that can detect an odor in vapors at a ratio of one particle to a million. Although the instruments have many uses, they are particularly important to our space program.

In satellites, they measure temperature, air pressure, radiation, and other vital information that they convert into radio signals that are sent back to receiving stations on the ground. Also, before launchings, our astronauts have tiny transducers taped to their bodies. These "read" their heart and pulse beats, their blood pressure, and their temperatures, and then radio the information back to earth. With this information we can tell whether or not an astronaut is suffering any ill effects from his voyage in space.

As you can see, your nervous system is surprisingly like an electrical hookup or electronic system. Because of this similarity, a remark made by a scientist years ago was much closer to the truth than he realized. He said, "We have now reached the point where we can practically say that when electricity stops, life stops." He was thinking of how much we depend on electricity for the operation of much of the world's machinery. He didn't know that we also depend on electricity for many of the operations of our own bodies.

It can truly be said that electricity was the most far-reaching discovery of the Industrial Revolution. The steam engine, the machine tools, the internal-combustion engine, all the many marvels of the period were extremely important. Nevertheless, none of them held the same exciting promise for today that electricity did.

Despite its many inventions and discoveries the Industrial Revolution would have been only moderately successful had it not been for one thing. This was the manufacturing method given to the world by the United States. It was known as the "American System."

10

THE AMERICAN SYSTEM

Eli Whitney's friends used to say of him, "He can make anything." As a teenager, Whitney earned a living by selling nails he pounded out on a homemade anvil. For a time, later, he became America's only maker of ladies' hatpins. In 1793, at age twenty-eight, he invented the cotton gin. With this machine for separating cotton fiber from its seeds, one slave could do what it took fifty to do by hand labor. The cotton gin made Whitney famous.

Five years later, the United States Government gave him a contract to make 12,000 muskets in two years, 4,000 to be delivered in the first year. This, despite the fact that he didn't have a gun factory and had never made a musket. He was awarded the contract only because of his fame as an inventor.

Whitney was to be paid 160,800 dollars, which made the order the country's biggest single financial deal for the year 1798. In the eyes of many people, the order was also the government's biggest blunder of the year—and not just because Whitney lacked experience with guns.

Accurate metalwork was unheard of in those days. If metalwork were done by hand, its accuracy would vary with the skill of the mechanic. If it were done by machine tools it would still be inaccurate. Recently invented machines for making other machines were still being run on a one-part-at-a-time basis.

Eli Whitney's early cotton-gin model as shown in a wood engraving of the nineteenth century.

The parts were almost always slightly different, since engineers hadn't yet learned how to make machine tools do absolutely precise work.

Because of these inaccuracies, when a machine or an implement like a musket was assembled, some parts always had to be hammered or filed to make them fit together. If a machine broke down, it had to go back to the shop, where a mechanic would make a new part to replace the damaged one. Spare parts were unheard of.

Things couldn't be manufactured in the same sense that they are manufactured today. They had to be put together individually by skilled mechanics; but there was only a handful of expert machinists in the infant republic. The gunsmiths among them could, at best, each make only one gun a week. So critics of the contract given to Whitney had reason to think it made no sense. As they saw it, if he could hire every gunsmith in the country, which was unlikely, he still couldn't produce 12,000 muskets in two years.

They underestimated their man. Whitney wasn't even thinking of gunsmiths. What he had in mind was a revolutionary new manufacturing system, which would enable an unskilled worker to make a product every bit as good as that made by an experienced machinist. Furthermore, he planned to make all the bits and pieces of his musket—triggers, barrels, stocks—so identical in size and shape that they could be switched from one gun to another, or be stored as spare parts. In today's language, he intended to "standardize" production by using "interchangeable" parts.

Whitney built a factory in Connecticut and began the difficult job of trying to realize his dream. First, he made a template for each individual musket part. (A template is a pattern, like a dress pattern, that is used as a guide when metal or wood has to be cut to a certain size and shape.) Whitney thought that if gunmetal were clamped on a workbench and a template were clamped on top of it, any unskilled worker could then cut the metal to pattern—*if* he had a cutting tool that could follow the lines of the template easily. Then Whitney erased the *if* by inventing such a device.

He cut a series of teeth in the rim of an iron wheel about the size of a bicycle sprocket. It looked like a gear but each tooth was curved, honed to a cutting edge, then hardened. As the wheel turned, one tooth after another struck the gunmetal a chisel-like blow. Each cutting blow was identical because the iron wheel had none of the unsteadiness that creeps into even the most experienced human hand. Because the wheel was power driven its rotary cutting action was continuous. Whitney's invention could do the same work as a pair of scissors in a dressmaker's hands. It could cut metal to pattern.

Whitney even made a template for his drill press to make certain each hole bored in a given musket part was correctly placed. With his various templates to guide them, his workmen didn't have to be particularly skillful. All they needed to do accurate work was their two hands. Thus, in a sense, his system made men as well as musket parts interchangeable. If one man quit, finding another was no great problem.

The final result was the first mechanized factory ever set up to make a product in large numbers from standardized parts. Such a factory has advantages others lack. With high-speed machinery, hundreds of parts can be made in the time it takes to make one by hand. The parts, as a result, cost much less than handmade ones. The things people want and need can be produced in much greater quantity and sold far more cheaply. Today, for example, almost everyone can enjoy television, whereas if TV sets had to be made by hand, only the very rich could afford them. The same can be said of almost everything we own.

Whitney's invention of the "American System," as it was then called, proved to be the magic key to making all sorts of things in previously undreamed of abundance. Today we call his system mass production and never give it a second thought. Yet, the invention forged a new way of life for the entire world. Some historians say that the main difference between our modern age and all others is that we engage in the mass production of goods.

Whitney didn't bring his dream to life as quickly as he had hoped. It took him eight years of hard work to perfect his complicated system, eight years rather than two to deliver 12,000 muskets. Then, after his factory was running smoothly, the government gave him a new contract. This time he produced 15,000 muskets in just under two years. It was the first instance of true mass production.

Whitney's system perfectly illustrates a point made earlier.

Since the 1700's seldom has any one man been able to take full credit for a major advance in technology. Whitney didn't invent the use of standardized parts. In the sixteenth century, the *Arsenal* shipyard in Italy built galleys of interchangeable parts. Later, Dutch shipbuilders used the same method to assemble fishing boats. Whitney, himself, knew that a few years before he opened his factory another inventor had tried, without success, to interest the French government in the manufacture of muskets made from identical parts.

This in no way lessens Whitney's importance. He may have followed in other men's footsteps, but they were faint footprints, and it was his genius that perfected the system.

Once Whitney had proved the worth of the American System, you'd think all manufacturers would immediately have turned to it. Not so. A great many in America did; it's true. But for half a century most English and European industrialists stubbornly ignored it. For instance, Whitney went into heavy production in 1811. Yet in the 1850's, the English army had to place a large order with United States armories for guns "made according to the American system of manufacture," because England's own gunsmiths still hadn't adopted mass-production methods.

Around 1850, too, a United States clockmaker sent a shipment of mass-produced brass clocks to England to be sold for 50 cents apiece (a half-dollar purchased a lot more then than it does now). Because the average hand-assembled English clock cost around 5 dollars the British government wouldn't let the 50-cent clocks go on sale. Britons thought the United States manufacturer was being unfair, that he had priced his clocks below their actual value to undersell English clockmakers and to gain a foothold in the British market.

When the English discovered that mass-produced clocks actually could be made and sold for a profit at a 50-cent price, they were dumbfounded. The incident, which caused a lot of talk among businessmen overseas, was one of several that taught foreign manufacturers something that should have been obvious to them. If they didn't adopt the American System, they were in danger of being driven out of business. As might have been expected, within a few years mass production was almost as common in England and Europe as it was in the United States.

The American System was our greatest single contribution to the Industrial Revolution. United States engineers and scientists, however, also played active roles in the perfection of the other major technical advances of the period: steam power, the internal-combustion engine, machine tools, and electric power.

All of the six basic machine tools invented in England, for instance, were improved by Americans. Whitney's rotary cutting head for following a template's guidelines was a brand-new addition to the "miller," or milling machine. Before Whitney's invention the miller's usefulness was limited. Afterwards, it could be used in so many ways in making machine parts that some people still insist it was Whitney who created the first milling machine worthy of the name.

In the field of steam power, most of us know that an American, Robert Fulton, invented the first practical steamship. While England introduced the locomotive, within ten years it had been so improved by Yankee engineers that United States "iron horses" were everywhere recognized as the world's best. Indeed, even England began to buy American-made locomotives. As for the steam engine, once James Watt's patent ran out a Philadelphia inventor, Oliver Evans, was free to try his hand at building a similar one. He developed an engine that was not only much smaller and less expensive, it also generated more power with an 8-inch piston stroke than a Watt engine did with a 6-foot stroke!

The pioneer American developer of the internal-combustion engine was Charles Duryea, who started out as a bicycle mechanic. Inspired by an account of the automobile Karl Benz was making in Germany, Duryea set out, in 1891, to build a better car and engine. Five years later he took one of his cars to England and entered it in a 52-mile road race. Many cars from France, Germany, and other countries were also entered in the contest. It turned out to be no contest, because Duryea crossed the finish line almost an hour ahead of his nearest rival!

Since that memorable day, American inventors have never stopped improving the internal-combustion engine. Since then, too, more than 220 million cars have been manufactured in the United States. And 86 million of those cars are still in use! This proves, if nothing else, that the American internal-combustion engine has incredible staying power.

Scientists in this country were leaders in putting the energy that first flowed from Faraday's generator to practical use. American inventors produced the electric light bulb and the telegraph. The most valuable single patent ever issued is U.S. Patent Office grant Number 174,465, given to Alexander Graham Bell in 1876 for his invention of the telephone. It was Lee De Forest, an American too, who created the first practical vacuum tube—a device of immeasurable value because it picks up and greatly magnifies even a weak electrical signal. Indeed, the vacuum tube has been called the world's "small, warm, glowing electronic heart," with good reason. It has turned out to be the key to most of the miracles of modern electronics, from radio and computers to television and radar.

Throughout the two centuries of the Industrial Revolution

American inventors made so many contributions, large and small, that it would be almost impossible to list them all. Their inventions ranged from the sewing machine, the typewriter, the thermos bottle, and a machine for making button holes, to the cooking range, the drip coffee pot, and the steam-heated radiator.

Even "crooked shoes," as they were first called, are an American invention. It may surprise you to learn that shoes especially designed to fit the right foot and the left foot were first introduced by a shoe manufacturer in Lynn, Massachusetts, in 1850.

Indeed, from The Miner's Friend of 1698 to the end of the Industrial Revolution, one invention bred another with almost unbelievable rapidity. Oddly enough, for a time this created a very real problem. Most inventions had to be manufactured in factories, so new factories sprang up like mushrooms. The more new factories there were, the more new workmen had to be hired. These workers had to be fed, but as often as not they were men who had given up growing foodstuffs on farms to work in factories to earn more money.

Yet, the keystone of civilization, as was pointed out earlier, has always been man's ability to produce enough surplus food to feed the vast and vital army of workers who engage in non-farming activities. As factories multiplied during the Industrial Revolution, they drew so many men away from farms that farmers were eventually faced with a serious labor shortage.

This was particularly true in America, especially at harvest time, because when a crop is ripe it must be harvested quickly. It is then that additional hands are most needed. Just when our rapidly spreading industrialization made the growing of more surplus food essential, our capability of growing it began to shrink. In fact, the labor shortage forced many farmers to cut back on the acreage they planted.

Had it not been for two American inventors it might have become a very serious problem. One of the inventors is still praised in history books. The other has been forgotten. The former was Cyrus McCormick, whose McCormick Reaper appeared in 1840. It was a horse-pulled harvesting machine, somewhat like an old-fashioned hand lawnmower blown up to giant size, with long, revolving, knifelike blades. With it, one man could harvest a field of grain much faster than a dozen men could do it with scythes and sickles. With it, too, farmers could stop cutting their acreage back and begin, instead, to clear and plant even more land. In this country, the production of wheat was tripled within a few years of the appearance of the McCormick Reaper. As the reaper found its way into overseas markets, production abroad increased, too.

Then a new problem arose. Encouraged by the reaper and the ever-growing demand for grain, our farmers began to plow up and plant the broad western prairies. This was land the cattle barons had long considered their private domain. Moreover, since it was a land of few trees, there was not enough wood for fence posts or fence rails. Farmers had no way to keep cattle from invading their fields to eat what grain they wanted and to trample the rest into the dirt. This brought farmers into constant and bitter conflict with cattlemen, sometimes even into battles with rifles and shotguns.

The situation could have had serious consequences. But just when matters were at their worst, a man you have never heard of invented something you probably never give a thought to, unless it scratches you or tears your shirt. It was barbed wire, invented in 1873 by Joseph Glidden of DeKalb, Illinois.

Cyrus Hall McCormick's reaper was invented in 1831.

Although barbed wire doesn't seem to be anything to get excited about, it actually ranks among man's major inventions. It is easy and inexpensive to fence in vast fields of grain with three strands of barbed wire and fence posts spaced far apart. Because of these advantages, barbed-wire fencing has made it possible to keep animals and crops apart on all of the world's humid grasslands—the lands that are especially well suited to both farming and cattle grazing. In a world that is wholly dependent on food surpluses, this is no small matter.

On our western prairies, for example, barbed-wire fencing tipped the scales in favor of the farmer. With it, he could protect his fields from the cattleman's roaming herds. Thus, barbed-wire spelled the difference between a thinly peopled open-range country and closely settled farmland. This farmland thrived, now producing such immense surpluses of food that it has earned the United States the title of "breadbasket of the world." As you may know, we now send grain to many of the world's hungry, underprivileged people. To countless thousands of people, barbed-wire fencing has meant, indirectly, the difference between starvation and survival. This alone is reason for giving this seemingly unimportant invention the recognition long due it.

Near the beginning of the Industrial Revolution, you'll recall, an English engineer wrote of his country, "Almost every Master Manufacturer hath a new invention of his own, or is daily improving on those of others." In 1900, at the end of the era, there was more truth than ever in his remark; it applied not only to England but to all industrialized nations. Recently, a historian wrote that at the end of the Industrial Revolution ". . . new inventive wonders were appearing so fast that people no longer wondered at them." *His* comment is much truer of today than it was in 1900.

We have now reached the point where new inventions appear so fast that no one can keep up with them. In Washington alone, the United States Patent Office has a backlog of 200,000 patent applications waiting to be acted on. Things are not much better in the world's other patent offices.

PART 4

11

THE AGE OF AUTOMATION

THE most complete study yet made of man's toolmaking—five thick volumes entitled *A History of Technology*—ends at the year 1900. The history's authors gave up at that point because, they said, ". . . the great technical complexity of modern industry makes it virtually impossible to tell its story in nontechnical terms."

Nevertheless, in a book attempting to show how tools shape our lives there is one present-day trend that can't be ignored, even though it is difficult to explain simply. It is automation.

There are many types of automation. They range from the pop-up toaster and the self-winding wristwatch to the automatic elevator. Another example is your mother's automatic washing machine. None of these would, however, excite an automation engineer because, as one of them says, "We're out to build entire factories that allow us to boast, 'Look, Ma, no hands!' "

An illustration of what excites him is a plant that can produce 90 percent of all the electric light bulbs used in the United States with the help of only fourteen employees! Automated machines now do all of the work that was formerly done by hundreds of men and dozens of nonautomated machines. The factory's fourteen employees are not routine workmen but automation specialists who merely keep a watchful eye on the production line. The only time their hands get dirty is when a machine breaks down.

This is the sort of automation that can't be ignored, because it will be as important to the future as the American System and machine tools were to the Industrial Revolution. In fact, you can be fairly certain that because of automation your adult life will differ considerably from your father's.

Think of the change the Industrial Revolution brought. Before 1900, half of the work in the United States was done by muscles, and men labored an average of seventy-two hours a week. In 1960, 99 percent of the work was done by machinery and power, and the workweek had shrunk to forty hours. Now, experts are saying that automation will bring the day when *no* muscle power will be needed in routine factory work! They also think that for a great many people the workweek will shrink to twenty hours.

This day will come, they believe, because automated machines are not only much faster and more reliable than machines run by men; they are also capable of manufacturing goods at much less cost. This is why they are slowly but surely doing away with many of the job opportunities and careers that were open to your father's generation. But while they are near-human enough to do a man's work, automated machines must be controlled and supervised and kept in running condition. Those who supervise them, however, must learn skills which were unknown before World War II. Thus to prepare yourself for a job in tomorrow's automated business world, you will almost certainly have to study some courses that didn't exist in your father's school days.

The language of automation is filled with phrases like "digital computation," "alphameric codes," "monolithic integrated circuitry," and "source language acronyms." This explains why the authors of *A History of Technology* threw up their hands in despair and quit.

Yet, if you think of automation in terms of your own body you can get a general idea of how it works. Each machine, for instance, has a metal framework, or chassis, which could be called a skeleton. It does its work with moving parts that can be compared to a man's arms and hands. If it is power driven it can also be said, in a sense, to have muscles.

To continue the comparison, an automated machine has, in addition, electronic eyes and other sense organs that enable it to see and know what it is doing. It has a nervous system made up of specially designed electronic circuits. These circuits feed coded information in the form of electronic signals, or pulses, into the machine to tell it what to do. And the machine's eyes, among other things, can tell when the machine isn't doing its job properly, then either stop it or correct the mistakes.

In Chapter 9 the point was made that your nerve-brain network closely resembles an electrical system. Your sense organs work like transducers, electromechanical devices that change one form of energy into another. When you touch something hot a set of transducing nerve fibers in your fingertips rushes an electronic warning signal through the "wiring" of your nervous system to your brain. After decoding the signal your brain sends a message back over your nerve circuit to your hand, ordering it to move. When you jerk your hand away from the heat you are converting your brain's electronic energy into muscular energy.

Compare the performance of your nerve-brain network with the way an automation system can react to a heat problem in a steel mill. In one of the mill's operations hot molten metal is poured into molds under the watchful "eyes" of transducers that measure both the heat and the rate of flow of the metal. If something goes wrong in the furnace and the metal begins to cool and flow too slowly, the transducers send electronic warning signals to an intricate device, which is the electrical "brain" in charge of the operation.

The brain decodes the signals, learns what is wrong, and reacts in a flash. It sends a message to one instrument with instructions to increase the heat of the furnace. Then it orders a second instrument to open the valves through which the metal is pouring a bit wider, so the cooling metal can flow more freely during the minutes it takes to raise the furnace heat to its normal level.

As you see, there are many similarities between the way automation operates and the way your body functions. You can see, too, that the mill's automated machinery has a built-in "nervous system" that enables it both to watch what it is doing and to know when either to stop or do something else. Engineers call this system "feedback." Feedback is the heart of automation, because it alone gives a machine the ability to react to the information its transducers feed it.

The simplest illustration of feedback is found in the thermostat, the transducer that controls the furnace in your home. A thermostat feeds information about room temperature to a furnace switch. If the thermostat is set at 70 degrees and the temperature falls below that, the tip of a coiled metal spring, which expands and contracts with changes in temperature, touches an electrical contact. This sends a signal to the switch that turns the furnace on. When the temperature rises to 70 degrees the spring expands and pulls away from the contact. This break in the circuit shuts off the furnace. There is, you see, a constant feedback of information between the thermostat and the furnace.

The principle of the thermostat was discovered in 1830; the

device itself was being manufactured in 1885; and its sales began to soar in 1906. Thus, it seems fairly certain that thermostats were both the first transducers and the first feedback devices to come into general use.

In the 1920's, many other transducers began to appear. Some were designed to measure pressure or weight, some, distance or speed or degrees of light and sound. Others were created to detect errors like overheating, or a decline in a generator's power output. In effect, they were all electric or mechanical instruments with which machines could see, hear, feel, or touch.

Originally, they were connected to dials or lights in such a way that they fed information only to the men who ran machines. (A flashing red light, for example, would warn a workman that his machine was overheated.) It took World War II to open engineers' eyes to the full possibilities of automatic feedback and to the fact that machines could be given electronic nervous systems that would function without human help.

The war led to an urgent demand for new weaponry, which speeded up research tremendously. Out of this research grew brilliant uses of feedback in automatic-detection systems, like radar and sonar, as well as target-tracking and automatic fire-control systems for big guns. Above all, there was the proximity fuse, whose radar feedback "told" an anti-aircraft shell's detonator when the shell was close enough to an enemy plane to be exploded with deadly effect. There was also the homing torpedo, with sonic "ears" that picked up the sound of an enemy warship's propellers, then fed the torpedo's automatic pilot the data it needed to guide the torpedo to its target.

The war's end marked the true beginning of the age of automation, because it freed scientists to put their new knowledge of feedback to peace-time uses. With peace, too, engineers found time to develop a language for communicating with machines—an obvious necessity if automation was to succeed. They found they could "tell" machines what to do and how to do it by means of a code that machines could, in a sense, read and understand.

Controlling a machine with the help of coded instructions had been done before, most notably by a French textile engineer, Joseph Jacquard. In order to weave intricate patterns into silk fabrics, in 1805 Jacquard designed a series of punched cards for guiding the operation of a loom with 1,200 needles. The cards were fed into the loom one-by-one, so that a new card would strike the needles with each pass of the shuttle. The solid part of the card would push aside certain needles, while the card's holes allowed the remaining needles to weave their colored threads into the fabric. It was a simple, yet effective, way of making a machine "obey" instructions.

An American who adapted Jacquard's punched cards to his own needs, Dr. Herman Hollerith, laid the foundation for the electronic machine-language we now use. The 1880 United States census had taken seven years to complete because all of the data on a population of 50 million people had to be hand-written on cards, then hand-counted and sorted. This gave the Census Bureau good reason to fear that, with the population swelling, it wouldn't be able to finish counting the 1890 census before the 1900 census came due.

Dr. Hollerith solved the problem by inventing a machine that completed the 1890 census of 62 million people in one-third the time it took to count 50 million in 1880. Following a carefully planned pattern, a hole was punched in each person's card to represent his sex, age, occupation, and other data. Then the card was placed over a series of tiny mercury-filled cups, and a lever lowered rows of telescoping pins to the card's surface. Wherever there was a hole, a pin passed through it to the mercury beneath. This closed an electrical circuit and allowed an electronic pulse to move a counter one position on a speedometerlike dial.

In addition to mechanizing the job of counting, Dr. Hollerith had demonstrated something vastly more important. He had shown that with patterns of punched holes that open and close electrical circuits you can operate machines automatically. Today, we still tell machines what they're to do in much the same way.

For simple jobs, in fact, punched cards are still used. More

INTERNATIONAL BUSINESS MACHINES CORPORATION

The early census-counting machine of Dr. Herman Hollerith.

complicated jobs, calling for lengthy sets of coded instructions, are handled by rolls of perforated paper tapes. For extremely complicated jobs, tapes bearing microscopic magnetized spots are used. On such tapes, coded patterns involving as many as 1,511 spots can be crowded into an inch of tape that holds only about 70 punched holes. The magnetized spots perform the same function as the holes. They flip switches on or off, to open or close electronic circuits.

There is another major difference today, too. Now, automated machines are usually operated by specially designed computers called "control computers." Control computers are interpreters that translate the coded instructions men feed into them into electronic signals that tell a machine what it is supposed to do. To experts, computers that control a single machine are simple devices compared to those that run a series of linked machines or, in rare cases, an entire factory. But if you aren't an expert no computer is simple; they are possibly the most complicated devices man has yet built.

Basically, though, all computers are made up of thousands of electronic circuits harnessed together in a bewildering maze. There are separate sets of circuits for each computer part, and trunklines through which signals flow from one part to another. The flow of electricity through each individual circuit is controlled by an electronic switch, which, in response to the signals it receives, either closes the circuit or breaks it.

A control computer's main parts are its input unit, its control unit, and its "memory," or information-storage unit. Coded instructions are fed into the computer through the input unit. When a roll of punched tape passes through this unit a circuit closes whenever a metal brush makes an electrical contact through a hole. This lets an electronic pulse, or signal, pass through the briefly closed circuit. Each hole's signal has a

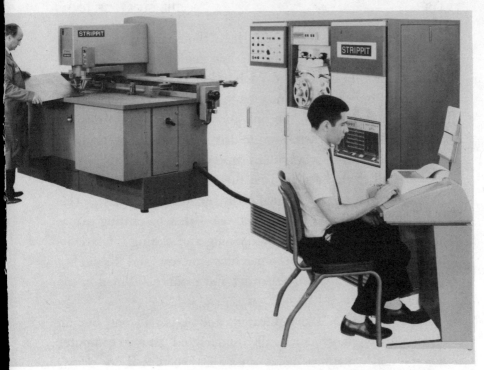

Commands are fed to this automated drill press from the input unit (right) and translated by the computer (center) into electrical impulses that guide the drill through its complex task.

meaning all its own, like a dot or dash in the Morse code. (A pulse only one-thousandth of a second long might be a dot, one lasting three-thousandths of a second, a dash.) A series of signals sent out by a specially arranged pattern of holes can be likened to a telegraph message spelled out in dots and dashes.

The messages carry electronic addresses as well as instructions and are sent to the control unit, which acts as the computer's mailman. Its first job is to deliver the messages to the specific network of circuits in the memory unit to which they are addressed. If a computer is controlling a single machine, there may be no more than four or five networks, or addresses, in its memory unit. There may be a thousand or more if the computer is running an assembly line made up of many different machines. In either case, each individual network to which an instruction is sent is harnessed to a single electric motor and is concerned only with the operation of that one motor. The motors, in turn, are those used to drive the moving parts of the machinery under the computer's supervision.

When all of the messages on the tape have been delivered, the control unit gets a signal, "Instructions completed." This frees the control unit for its next job—that of putting a machine to work. It does this by opening and closing the circuits that supply electricity to the machine's motors, and it switches them on and off in the exact order and manner outlined in the instructions.

All of this sounds complicated, and it is. No one but an electronics engineer can really understand *how* a computer works—and sometimes he becomes a little confused, too. However, the *way* a computer works can be illustrated by analyzing a routine machine-shop job.

Let's assume that 26 holes have to be drilled in the metal base-plate of the chassis of a tv set so the set's working parts can be anchored with bolts and rivets. Because some of the holes have to be one-eighth, some one-quarter, and some three-eighths of an inch in diameter, we'll use a computer-controlled eight-spindle turret drill. This is a standard machine tool that has eight arms, or spindles, sticking out of a rotating turret, like spokes from the hub of a wheel, with each spindle holding a different-size bit.

Beneath the turret is a table to which the base plate is clamped. Under this table are three worm drives. (The threaded steel bar you turn to open and close the jaws of a vise is a worm drive.) With these worm drives, the table can be moved sideways, backward or forward, and up or down. The table is thus able to move the base plate so that any spot on its surface can be positioned directly under a drill bit.

The drill's moving parts are driven by electric motors. There is a motor that turns the bits, one for each worm drive, and one that turns the turret to bring into place whichever bit is needed. Each of the five motors, remember, takes its orders from a specific group of circuits in the computer's memory unit.

How do we start? First, a set of instructions is punched out on a roll of tape by a technician known as a "programmer." The tape is then fed into the input unit. For this job about 10 feet of coded tape will be needed. It will pass through the input unit at a rate of about 20 inches per second. The electronic impulses sent through the holes in the tape can travel nearly a foot in one-billionth of a second. And the computer, which works much faster than the human brain, can absorb hundreds of instructions a second. So the full set of instructions will be stored in the computer's memory in about the time it takes you to read this paragraph.

A 7 or 8-inch piece torn off the tape would look like this:

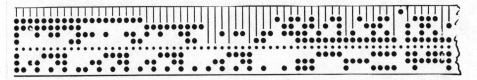

Assuming this fragment contains the computer's first instructions, a translation of the code into English might read as follows:

1) Table holding base plate is to be moved 11 inches to the left by worm-drive A. Close the circuits that feed power to the motor of worm-drive A. 2) Instruct transducer that measures the table's sideward movement to feed back a signal to stop worm-drive A when it has moved 11 inches. 3) Worm-drive B is to move table forward 5 inches. Close circuits to its motor. 4) Transducer measuring forward movement is to feed back stop signal when table has moved 5 inches. 5) With base plate now in position for first drilling operation, turn spindle turret to bring one-quarter inch bit into working position.

The next few inches of tape would carry instructions for starting the motor that turns the bit, for raising the table to bring the base plate to bear against the revolving bit, for lowering the table to free the plate of the bit after the hole is drilled, and, finally, an order to shut off the motor turning the bit. The remainder of the tape would carry similar sets of instructions for each of the other 25 holes to be drilled, and would end with the final signal, "Instructions completed." Only at this point, when all of the instructions have been stored in the memory, would the control unit begin to operate the drill press. Following orders to the letter, the control unit would begin to open and close the circuit's feeding power to the drill's five motors in the exact sequence called for in the instructions.

Now that you've seen how a small computer guides one machine through a routine job, you can probably imagine how a bigger computer controls a series of linked machines. With a much longer set of instructions stored in a larger memory, the drill press computer could, for example, order a mechanical hand to carry the base plate from the drill to a machine that would cut some needed slots in it, then to a machine that would automatically rivet the picture tube support-frame to the plate, and so on until the TV set is completely assembled.

Computers not only control production in television and radio factories, and in steel mills and plants that make electric-light bulbs. They can also be programmed to guide almost any machine or series of machines through an almost endless variety of tasks.

Automobile manufacturing is heavily automated. Engine blocks enter a production line as solid chunks of metal and come off the line fully machined, without being touched by a hand. A car's body can be completely assembled as a conveyor belt carries its parts from one to another of a dozen-odd automated machines that do everything from welding the sections of the body together to folding over the rain channels on the car-top.

Computers even bake cakes by the hundreds of thousands. In one large bakery, a computer checks the program stored in its massive memory for each day's recipes, then sets in motion machines that mix batter by the ton for twelve different kinds of cakes. After that the computer masterminds a conveyor belt that carries the cakes through an oven, a chamber that cools them so they can be iced, and a quick-freezing unit. With its transducers the computer also sees to it that the temperatures in the oven and the cooling and quick-freezing units never rise above or fall below a set level. Once the cakes are frozen the computer not only handles their packaging but also runs the automatic cranes and lifts that store them in their warehouse bins!

To mention only a few more examples, computers control manufacturing processes in chemical and brick-making plants, oil refineries, and paper and cement mills. They run the machines that fill milk containers and soft-drink bottles, and regulate the flow of electricity in our power lines and the mixing and cooking of the ingredients in canned soups. Even the hot dog has been automated. One manufacturer has an assembly line of machines that automatically produce weiners, from raw meat to plastic-wrapped packages, at the rate of 36,000 an hour. There is, in fact, almost no end to the list of goods computers are producing.

Since control computers and their slave machines are even now manufacturing everything from cakes to cars and cement, it's obvious that they have already become necessary to our way of life. However, it isn't only because they can make things without man's help. Their true importance lies in the fact that they produce goods with a speed and in quantities that wouldn't have been thought possible twenty years ago. That is why expert after expert has said that the computer holds "more promise for the human race than any other invention in history." It is why other experts have said, "If the computer didn't exist we would have to invent it. It's a tool we have to have."

The reason we have to have it is simple. The world's population is growing at the explosive rate of more than 70 million people a year—at a time when we aren't even producing and distributing enough of the necessities of life to supply the needs of the poor and underprivileged people now alive, much less the luxury items they want and deserve as much as any of us. As computerized automation, with its enormous production capabilities, grows and spreads, we may in time be able to meet mankind's increasing demands for the material blessings of life. That is why the promise of automation is so tremendous. With its help man may someday be able to fulfill an old dream —the dream of abundance for all and an end to poverty.

First, though, we have to find a sure answer to a vital question: Do we have the fuel and the power we need to run a fully industrialized world?

A modern automated wiener plant produces ten continuous belts of wieners, shown here emerging from the "stripper." Wieners were in cellulose casings, which are removed by the strippers to produce the skinless weiner.

12

ENERGY BY BOMBARDMENT

Now that we've tamed the energy of steam, electricity, coal, and fuel oil, you might think our power needs are solved for all time. Not so. Coal and oil, known as fossil fuels because they are ancient substances embedded in the earth, can never be replaced once they're used. They're being used so fast that France, England, Italy, and Sweden, have already all but exhausted their coal supplies. Moreover, along with most European countries they also have to rely on oil imported from overseas. As for the United States, rich though our natural resources are, it's considered doubtful that our readily obtainable fossil fuels will last more than another hundred years.

The trouble is that mankind is presently burning more than a million barrels of oil each hour! An estimated trillion barrels remain in the earth, it's true. Even so, it is feared that by 1980 oil production may begin to decline. And while the world's coal reserve is considerably larger, much of it is difficult to mine and a good deal of it is buried in faraway places. So in time coal may cost more to mine than it is worth.

Our massive consumption of fossil fuels is largely the result of the expanding demand for electricity, which has become our most important power source. Most electricity is made by burning coal or oil to produce the heat that converts water into steam, which, in turn, drives the generators that create electricity. (Hydroelectric plants supply only a small portion of the world's electricity.)

In heavily industrialized countries, where the demand for electricity doubles every ten years, the consumption of both coal and oil is rapidly increasing. When the underdeveloped countries, with their billions of people, become industrialized, the rate of consumption will take a frightening jump. Partially developed Pakistan, for example, now uses twenty times the electricity it used in 1947. You can see why man's hunger for electricity may, within a few decades, be too great for coal and oil to satisfy, and why an urgent search for new sources of energy is under way.

The search has led France to build the first sea-coast power plant, at enormous cost, for harnessing the energy of the tides. In this plant, as the tides ebb and flow they turn hydroelectric generators. An Italian power plant has gone to the dangerous extreme of tapping an active volcano to get the heat necessary for its operation. Attempts have also been made to draw heat from a few of the boiling-hot springs that dot the earth.

For years, too, men have been trying to trap the sun's energy. As you know from getting sunburned, even though the sun is 93 million miles away its rays strike the earth with considerable heat. Indeed, in three days the sun sends us as much energy in the form of heat and light as would be produced by burning the earth's entire oil and coal reserves and all of the wood in its forests.

In experiments, small steam engines have been run by sunlight, with the help of curved mirrors that focus the sun's rays on their boilers. In other experiments, concentrated sunlight has been used to cook food, heat houses, and even melt metals. But the sun's rays aren't easily captured, and no practical way has as yet been found for stockpiling their energy. It is generally believed that solar energy isn't likely to be tapped on any meaningful scale in this generation or the next.

Fortunately, though, we have here on earth one tremendous source of energy that may supply our power needs for centuries after we run out of coal and oil. Most people call it atomic energy. Scientists call it nuclear energy, for reasons to be made clear.

You have heard about the atom bomb all of your life. You probably know that when an atom bomb explodes its heat is so intense it reduces steel to vapor in a flash and also generates shock waves of expanding hot air so violent they destroy everything standing in their path. You may not know that in recent years a device has been developed for taming the terrifying destructive power of the atom and converting it into an enormously valuable fuel.

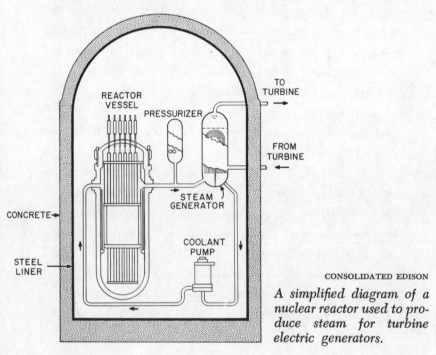

CONSOLIDATED EDISON

A simplified diagram of a nuclear reactor used to produce steam for turbine electric generators.

The device, called a reactor, is in a broad sense a furnace that "burns" atomic fuels. Although two other atomic fuels are sometimes used, uranium is the metal most often consumed. Uranium was the material used in the two atom bombs that ended World War II. As you might expect, uranium makes as incredible a fuel as it does an explosive. One cubic foot of uranium, for example, has the same energy content as 1,700,000 tons of coal, or 7,200,000 barrels of oil, or 32 billion cubic feet of natural gas!

Uranium is the most commonly used atomic fuel because it has a unique atom. All-matter is made up of atoms that are so small that a square inch of stone may hold 2 billion trillion of them. In turn, all atoms are made up of even smaller subatomic particles that are organized in much the same way as our solar system. That is, some of the subatomic particles are grouped solidly together to form what is known as an atom's nucleus —which can be compared to the sun—while other particles spin around this nuclear "sun" like planets in orbit.

The particles making up the nucleus are held together in the iron grip of an unimaginably powerful force, and scientists ruefully admit that they still don't know what this mysterious binding force is. They do know, though, that it is the root of what we commonly call atomic energy, because to create this energy you first have to split apart an atom's nucleus. When you do, the unknown force holding the nucleus together is suddenly released in the form of thermal, or heat, energy. It is heat energy millions of times greater than man has ever before known. And it can be converted to usable power for ordinary steam engines and turbines.

What makes the uranium atom unique is its all-important nucleus, which is more massive than that of any other natural atom. Thus, its nucleus offers the best target in nature for bom-

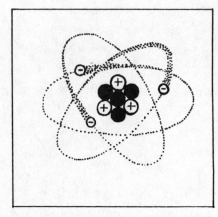

⊕ PROTON
● NEUTRON
⊖ ELECTRON

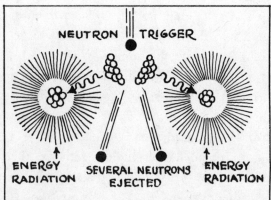

NEUTRON TRIGGER

ENERGY
RADIATION

SEVERAL NEUTRONS
EJECTED

ENERGY
RADIATION

How fission works.

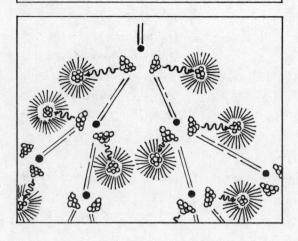

bardment. The secret of unleashing atomic energy lies in a complex process known as neutron bombardment.

In this process, a mass of uranium is exposed to salvos of subatomic particles called neutrons. When a neutron strikes the nucleus of one of the trillions of atoms in a chunk of uranium, the bombarded atom splits in two. As it flies apart, the atom releases its tremendous store of heat energy. What is equally important, as the nucleus breaks up it sets free two or more of the neutrons imprisoned in its core. The freed neutrons shoot into nearby atoms. These atoms then split and release more neutrons. They, in turn, bombard their neighboring atoms, which then shoot off more neutrons, and so on and on to set up what is called a chain reaction.

Since the successive steps in the chain occur at intervals of about one-millionth of a second, you can see that within a second or two a staggering number of atoms will be bombarded and an equally staggering amount of energy released. In an atom bomb, the chain reaction is allowed to run wild through trillions upon untold trillions of energy-packed atoms, because the end result desired is a violent explosion.

In a reactor, however, the opposite is true. Here the chain reaction is so carefully controlled that an explosion is impossible. The control is achieved in two ways. First, the uranium in a reactor's core—which could be likened to a furnace's firebox—is surrounded with a *moderator*. The moderator's role is to slow down the salvos of bombarding neutrons. Materials as simple as water and the graphite used in "lead" pencils are highly effective moderators.

The second method of curbing a chain reaction is through the use of *control rods* that regulate the "population" of neutrons inside the reactor's core. Made of materials that absorb subatomic particles, the rods are, in effect, blotters that soak up unwanted neutrons. Thus, through the use of moderators and control rods a deadly explosive can be converted into a fuel so potent that a single pound of it can produce as much energy as 1,440 tons of coal or 32,000 gallons of oil.

At the moment, though, we aren't getting all the energy we should get from uranium because present-day reactors waste 65 percent or more of the power locked in their atomic fuel. This is because atomic science is just emerging from the experimental stage, and we still have a lot to learn about building reactors. Just as modern automobile engines get far more horsepower out of a gallon of gasoline than those made during the Industrial Revolution, it is merely a question of time until much better reactors are built. Many new designs are even now being tested. If some of them live up to their promise, mankind may never again have to worry very much about power.

By ordinary engineering standards any device that wastes 65 percent of its power is absurdly impractical. Nevertheless, the use of reactors is mushrooming so fast that the International Atomic Energy Agency says it is "almost impossible" to keep track of their spread, which is proof, if any is needed, that atomic fuel is too extraordinary to be judged by the usual standards. As a matter of fact, under many circumstances it gives you more for your money than fossil fuels even when most of its energy is wasted—and a pound of refined uranium ore costs about 165 dollars, or nearly one-third as much as gold!

The first commercial atom-fueled atomic-power plant went into operation in England in 1956, the second, in this country in 1958. By 1967, the number had grown to seventy-five plants, either in operation or being built, in twenty-five foreign countries, with many others in the planning stage. In the United States, fourteen plants were producing electricity in 1967, thirteen more were under construction, and another thirty-two were in the blueprint stage. From now on, it's obvious, more and more often it will be the atom that responds when we flick the electrical switches upon which we are so deeply dependent.

Nor is the promise of the atom limited to the generation of electricity. Many atom-powered vessels now range the seas. The first to be launched, in 1962, was the U.S.S. *Savannah,* a merchant ship whose atomic fuel gives her a 350,000-mile crusing range, compared to 7,000 miles with ordinary fuel. (Unfortunately, as the first of her kind she was the victim of design errors that have made her unable to pay her way as a cargo ship, and there is talk of putting her in mothballs in 1970). The Russians have an ice-breaker, *Lenin,* that consumes a mere two ounces of nuclear fuel a month and can stay at sea for two years without refueling. Our navy has several atomic-powered surface ships. And both the United States and Russian navies have large fleets of submarines that can steam more than 96,000 miles on one nuclear-fuel load.

Furthermore, space engineers agree that manned flights to distant Mars and other remote planets, which would last two or more years, will be possible only with the help of atomic fuel, because it weighs so little and has such a long life. The United States has already tested an experimental spaceship reactor built into a rocket engine that is only 22-feet tall, with encouraging results.

While it may be hard to imagine, tiny reactors to provide power to keep an artificial heart beating are in the testing stage, too. What is more, the president of the American Heart Association says that atom-powered artificial hearts may be available within your lifetime. In fact, he thinks it "inevitable" that surgeons will someday routinely replace diseased hearts with atomic ones.

Model of a reactor to be built into a rocket engine.

Nonmilitary use of the atom's explosive power is also under study. Since a single explosion can move millions of tons of earth, serious thought is being given to deepening harbors and building canals with "atomic excavations." It may be, too, that with underground atom blasts we can set free oil and natural gas deposits that are now beyond our technological reach.

To find out if it is possible, a series of test shots will be set off in certain Rocky Mountain regions where trillions of cubic feet of gas and billions of barrels of oil lie locked in deep underground rock formations in such a way that they can't be tapped by ordinary drilling methods. The first test of the series, called Project Gasbuggy, was set off 4,240 feet beneath the bed of lonely Leandro Canyon, New Mexico, in 1968. Early indications are that the atomic blast did release the immense reservoir of gas buried beneath the canyon floor. However, it still remains to be seen whether the experiment was a practical success, because government experts say it will take a year or two to determine whether or not the level of radioactivity of the freed gas is harmless.

If Project Gasbuggy and the remaining test shots in the series do succeed, then the atom's awesome power will enable us to reach many currently untouchable fuel reservoirs, and our fossil fuel reserves will be increased tremendously.

When you think of its many and vast potentials, you can easily understand why nuclear energy is expected to play a vital role in mankind's future—and on a boundless stage that reaches into outer space as well as across all of the earth's continents and oceans.

13

LIGHT:
A TOOL OF THE FUTURE

NUCLEAR energy is by no means the end of the atom's story, because a strange new chapter was added to it in 1954, with the discovery of a totally different type of atomic energy.

All atoms, you'll remember, are made up of subatomic particles, with most of them forming a nuclear "sun" around which the remainder spin like planets in orbit. The orbiting particles give off the forms of energy we know as heat, light, sound, and electricity.

In 1954, a way was found to transform the energy of some of the orbiting particles into a unique kind of light. Of all the many technological discoveries of this century, it is certainly the oddest. It may also turn out to be one of the most useful. This new form of light is so powerful it can and has reached the moon. In addition, it is so fiery it can burn through asbestos and 4-inch-thick fire bricks as if they were tissue paper and can also crumble rocks of solid granite.

This fantastic light is generated by an instrument called a "laser." Just as uranium is best suited to the production of nuclear energy, only a few gases and crystals lend themselves to the generation of laser energy. The two most commonly used lasers are: (1) a glass tube filled with either helium, nitrogen, or carbon dioxide gas; and (2) a rod of synthetic, or man-made, ruby crystal enclosed in an enameled steel box. Both types have one thing in common, special shutterlike devices through which they release their light.

When the gases or ruby crystals are exposed to intense bolts of light, somewhat like those given off by flash-bulbs, an extraordinary phenomenon occurs. There are no nontechnical words to describe this phenomenon. The best explanation scientists can offer us is that the light bolts so "excite" the subatomic particles in the material being lased that they work themselves up to a much-higher-than-normal energy level. Then when they "relax" back to their normal state, they discharge the excess energy they've built up, in the form of light waves.

This is, in fact, exactly what happens in an ordinary fluorescent lamp. The light it gives off is energy escaping from particles of mercury vapor that have been excited by a current of electricity. The lamp's light is, however, just the normal light with which we are all familiar. It is ordinary white light that shoots from a bulb in all directions and often spends it energy so quickly that it is exhausted before it reaches the farthest, darkest corners of a room. A laser, on the other hand, prevents light from spreading out and wasting its energy. Instead, it concentrates and strengthens light to an almost unbelievable degree.

To understand how a laser concentrates light, you must remember that all light travels in waves, like ripples on a pond. The distance from one wave crest to the next is called a wavelength. And because ordinary white light is made up of many waves having different wavelengths, the waves tumble over each other as they travel helter-skelter in every direction. But inside a laser there is a mechanism that holds light down to a single wavelength, with all of the waves moving in one direction. The result is a light whose waves never collide but instead lend each other strength, like soldiers marching in lockstep.

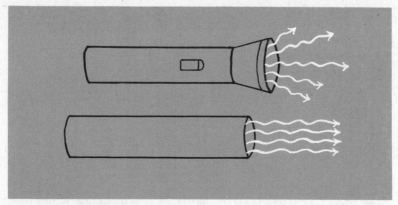

An ordinary flashlight projects incoherent light of many different wavelengths in many directions. Laser light is all one wavelength and travels in one direction over long distances.

Thus they can travel in an incredibly straight and narrow line for immense distances without wasting their energy by fanning out as automobile headlights and flashlight beams do.

At long range, for example, when traveling 254,000 miles to the moon a laser beam lights up a spot only two or three miles wide. If an ordinary searchlight could reach the moon, its ray would spread out more than 25,000 miles. At short range, a laser can focus light through a hole only fifty-millionths of an inch in diameter and, at the same time, generate a heat of 32,000 degrees, three times the temperature of the sun. (Even ordinary light rays generate intense heat when focused to a pinpoint, as you know if you've ever burned a hole in a piece of paper with sunlight focused through a magnifying glass.)

Lasers run in sizes as small as a pencil to more than 10 yards long. Their practical value is so great that many experts expect laser manufacturing to be our next billion-dollar industry. It could be, for as one engineer says, "The uses to which the laser may be put are so many and varied as to suggest magic."

Because they can focus intense heat on very tiny areas, lasers are already being used to weld the intricate circuits needed in many complicated electronic devices and in spacecraft. Many people have been saved from blindness by a small surgical laser whose shutter clicks at the rate of one-thousandth of a second as it "spot welds" a loosened retina back onto an eye-ball.

The laser has been a godsend to the American Telephone and Telegraph Company. Each year the company needs 30 million miles of copper wire as thin as a human hair for use in its telephone system. The wire is made by drawing softened copper through tiny holes drilled in diamonds, the world's hardest substance. Formerly it took a workman, using a steel pin coated with olive oil and abrasive diamond dust, two days to drill a hole in just one of the 4,000 diamonds the company wears out annually. With the heat from a laser beam focused down to 1/400 of an inch in diameter, a man can now drill the hole in two minutes.

Use is also being made of the fact that a laser's straight-line beam is the most accurate measuring "yardstick" ever known, its margin of error being only one-eighth of an inch in 18 miles. For this reason, on big construction jobs laser-beaming instruments are beginning to replace the up-to-now standard measuring tool, the surveyor's transit. Lasers have also been used to check the accuracy with which both pipelines and ships' keels have been laid. In one instance, too, with the help of a laser beam a 280-ton boring machine dug a 2-mile tunnel without once straying more than one-half inch from its path. Before it was given a laser to guide it, the machine often drifted 3 inches off course in an advance of only five feet.

As a measuring device the laser is also more precise than radar. With a radar, the time an electronic pulse takes to reach a target and return tells us how far away the target is. A flash of light from a laser bounces back from a target in the same way, but with far greater accuracy. In tracking a satellite only 100 miles out in space, for example, a radar has an error of about 20 feet. However, if a satellite is equipped with light-reflecting mirrors a laser range-finder can measure its distance from the earth to within 6 inches.

Because of the laser's great precision, the United States Army is experimenting with the use of lasers as artillery range finders. (Some, it is said, are already being field-tested in Vietnam.) The Army also has a 25-pound backpack infantry laser with a 4-inch antenna that does the same job as a conventional radar with a 60-foot-wide antenna.

Now in the development stage are lasers designed to crumble the solid rock through which tunnels must often be dug. Surgeons are testing lasers that cut out a growth like a tumor and cauterize the wound at the same time, thus stopping the flow of blood. Television-set manufacturers think specially designed lasers may be able to outperform standard picture tubes. In fact, in an experimental demonstration one company successfully projected a 3 by 5 foot picture onto a wall screen with a laser TV tube.

Also in the testing stage are lasers for such widely different uses as drilling teeth and erasing typing mistakes. (The black ink of a misspelled word absorbs the laser beam and is vaporized by its heat, while the paper goes unscorched because, being white, it has a mirrorlike quality that reflects the beam.) A far more important mistake may soon be "erased" by lasers too, with the help of an automobile range-finder now being road-tested. This laser is connected to a car's braking system, and when a careless driver makes the mistake of closing in on the car ahead too fast for safety, the laser automatically applies his brakes.

There is one possible use for the laser, however, that scientists don't like to talk about and for a good reason. The intensely fiery and far-reaching beam thrown out by a high-power laser has an obvious potential for destroying both enemy soldiers and approaching enemy missiles. There is no question that the world's military powers are exploring this possibility. It may be that the laser will become the death ray which until now has existed only in science fiction.

It is probable, though, that lasers will play their most important role in the field of communications, because light waves can carry sound in much the same way that it is carried on radio waves. At present we send messages by radio waves that are 300 yards long, or by microwaves about an inch long. Yet, there are lasers that can carry data on wavelengths only twenty-seven-*millionths* of an inch long. Obviously, too, the faster any message-carrying wave vibrates, or moves, the more data it can carry, and laser waves move a billion times faster than ordinary radio waves. This means that a single laser beam is capable of carrying every radio message, TV picture, and telephone call transmitted in the world on any given day! To put it another way, in a fraction of a second the beam could transmit the entire text of the *Encyclopaedia Britannica*.

The laser's communications capabilities are so enormous that we can't possibly make full use of them. It is no great problem to connect, say, Chicago and New York with a 2-inch plastic tube, equipped with mirrors to reflect the laser beam around corners. (The tube would prevent atmospheric conditions from scattering the beam's light rays.) Yet no more than a tiny fraction of this line could ever be used. In the entire world only about 25 million telephone calls are made daily. And a Chicago–New York laser-line could handle five times that many, all at once! Still, with telephone lines as overcrowded as they are, in time we'll probably have to turn to laser-lines.

The United States Navy is trying to develop a laser system for sending underwater messages between submarines, which has never before been possible. But outer space is the ideal region for laser communication. This is because space has no atmosphere, and thus no rain to scatter light rays and no clouds or fog to absorb them. Lasers are being designed for carrying messages between spaceships and for sending data from deep-space probes back to earth. In fact, beginning with the Gemini VII flight in 1965, our astronauts have, on several occasions, talked to their ground stations with the help of lasers.

It is possible too that lasers will play yet another role in our space program. Orbiting satellites are sometimes pushed out of orbit and miles closer to the earth by the sun. Few people realize that sunlight can shove or thrust. But like all energy, sunlight has weight. On earth the weight of the sun's light falling at noon on a city block is estimated to be equal to the weight of a cigarette paper lying on the sidewalk. However, outside the earth's atmosphere, where satellites travel, the thrust of the sun's light is far more powerful.

The time will probably come when it will be important to keep certain satellites in an exact, never-changing orbit. One such satellite would be a commercial navigation satellite for guiding ships and airplanes to their destinations. When that day comes, scientists will be prepared. They have already figured out a way to build a laser with a beam strong enough to overcome the sun's pressure and push a satellite back on course.

As it stands, an invention whose usefulness ranges from correcting a satellite's orbit to the erasure of a typist's mistake must be regarded as one of the greatest technical achievements in history. And this is only the beginning! As one of the leading authorities in the field says, "Lasers unquestionably

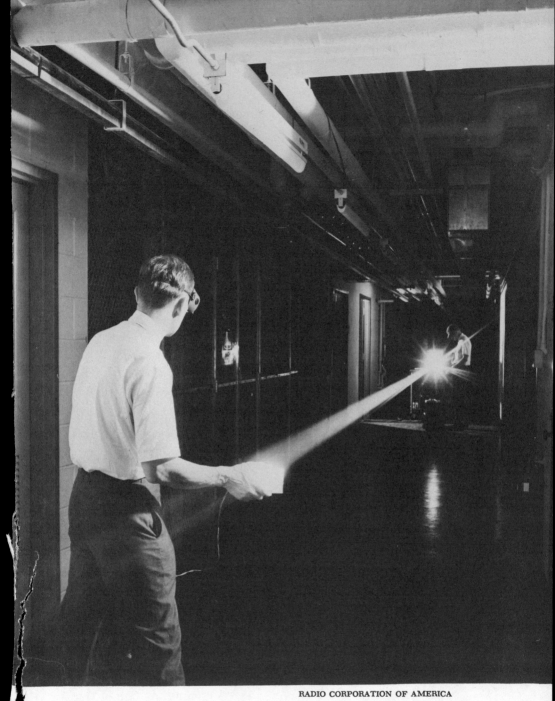

A *scientist checks the power density of a laser beam, which will one day be used to track space vehicles 100 miles above the earth.*

have uses that we haven't as yet even dreamed of. As a matter of fact, present-day lasers are as primitive as airplanes were in 1910. So you can be sure that their future is as bright as their brilliant light."

Extraordinary as it is, the laser will not be the last and final word in the story of man's toolmaking. That word will never be written. For as we have seen in the long journey from the pebble tool and the cave, technology is ever-changing. So you can be certain, even as you read this, that somewhere inventors are exploring ideas equally startling and revolutionary as those that led to automation, nuclear energy, and the laser. It is possible, too, that the genius of some as yet unsung inventor may one day change and enrich your life as much as the plow altered and improved the lives of your primitive forefathers.

Even if this shouldn't come to pass, the debt we owe history's long line of toolmakers is already greater than many of us realize. Thanks to them and the everincreasing abundance they have made possible, economists estimate that 40 percent of the world's population now enjoys an even higher standard of living than that enjoyed by the richest one percent of the people who lived prior to 1900.

Hopefully, too, the abundance our technology has made possible will soon put an end to the poverty and the hunger that still afflict the remaining 60 percent of the world's people. Then —but not until then—the century-old words of an American writer, Henry Ward Beecher, will come true: "He that invents a tool or a machine contributes to the well-being of all mankind."

BIBLIOGRAPHY

Adler, Irving, *Tools in Your Life*. New York: The John Day Company, 1956.

Asimov, Isaac, *The Intelligent Man's Guide to Science*. New York: Basic Books, Inc., 1960.

Barnett, Lincoln, *The Epic of Man*. New York: Time-Life Books, 1962.

Barrow, George, *Your World in Motion*. New York: Harcourt, Brace & World, Inc., 1956.

Bastian, Hartmut, *And Then Came Man*. New York: The Viking Press, 1964.

Becker, Beril, *Mechanical Man*. New York: G. P. Putnam's Sons, 1959.

— Brinton, Crane, Christopher, John B., and Wolff, Robert Lee, *A History of Civilization*. Englewood Cliffs, N.J.: Prentice-Hall, Inc., 1955.

Burck, Gilbert, and the editors of *Fortune, The Computer Age*. New York: Torchbooks, Harper & Row, 1965.

— Burns, William A., *Man and his Tools*. New York: Whittlesey House, 1956.

Childe, V. Gordon, *Man Makes Himself*. New York: Mentor Books, 1963.

Collins, A. Frederick, *The Amateur Machinist*. New York: The New Home Library, 1942.

Deetz, James, *Invitation to Archaeology*. Garden City, N.Y.: The Natural History Press, 1967.

Derry, T. K., and Williams, Trevor I., *A Short History of Technology*. New York and Oxford: Oxford University Press, 1961.

Englebardt, Stanley L., *Computers*. New York: Pyramid Publications, Inc., 1965.

Hedger, George A., ed., *An Introduction to Western Civilization*. New York: Doubleday, Doran & Company, Inc., 1939.

Hogerton, John F., *Atomic Fuel*. Washington, D.C.: Division of Technical Information, Atomic Energy Commission, 1964.

———— *Nuclear Reactors*. Washington, D.C.: Division of Technical Information, Atomic Energy Commission, 1965.

LaBarre, Weston, *The Human Animal*. Chicago: The University of Chicago Press, 1954.

Laird, Donald A. and Eleanor C., *How to Get Along With Automation*. New York: McGraw-Hill Book Company, 1964.

Lips, Dr. Julius E., *The Origin of Things*. New York: A. A. Wyn, Inc., 1956.

Meyer, Jerome S., *Machines*. Cleveland and New York: The World Publishing Company, 1958.

Moore, Ruth, *Evolution*. New York: Life Nature Library, Time-Life Books, 1962.

Morison, Samuel Eliot, *The Oxford History of the American People*. New York: Oxford University Press, 1965.

Muller, Herbert J., *Freedom in the Ancient World*. New York: Harper & Brothers, 1961.

———— *Freedom in the Western World*. New York: Harper & Row, 1963.

———— *Freedom in the Modern World*. New York: Harper & Row, 1966.

Newman, James R., ed., *The Harper Encyclopedia of Science*. New York: Harper & Row, 1963.

Oakley, Kenneth P., *Man the Toolmaker*. Chicago: The University of Chicago Press, 1964.

O'Brien, Robert, *Machines*. New York: Life Science Library, Time-Life Books, 1964.

Rolt, L. T. C., *A Short History of Machine Tools*. Cambridge: The M. I. T. Press, Massachusetts Institute of Technology, 1965.

———— *Science and Discovery*. Englewood Cliffs, N.J.: International Graphic Society, 1960.

Shapley, Harlow, Rapport, Samuel, and Wright, Helen, eds., *A Treasury of Science*. New York: Harper & Brothers, 1954.

Singer, C., ed., *A History of Technology*. Oxford: Clarendon Press, 1954–1958 (5 volumes).

Soulard, Robert A., *A History of the Machine*. New York: Hawthorn Books Inc., 1963.

Thirring, Hans, *Energy for Man*. New York and Evanston: Harper & Row, 1962.

Wilson, Mitchell, *American Science and Invention*. New York: Bonanza Books, 1960.

INDEX

Page numbers in italics refer to illustrations.

The Author

James Poling was born in Lima, Ohio, and was graduated from the University of Michigan, *summa cum laude*, with an A.B. degree. He is a man of a great many interests; chief among them are marine biology and natural science.

A free-lance writer, his articles have appeared in every major magazine. He has written four books for adults, and his previous children's books are *The Man Who Saved Robinson Crusoe* and *Animals in Disguise*.

Mr. Poling makes his home in New York City with his wife, Patricia.